A Collector's Guide and History to Lionel Trains

Volume IV:
1970-1980

By Tom McComas & James Tuohy

PHOTOGRAPHY BY DONALD C. NEAL & TOM McCOMAS

To the aunts

Ann, Dorothy, Florence,
Helen, Julia, Libby,
Mildred and Vern

God love them

Library of Congress catalog number: 75-189 999
Published by TM Productions, Box 189, Wilmette, Illinois 60091
Copyright© 1980 by Thomas W. McComas and James Tuohy
Printed in the United States of America.
First printing March, 1980

CONTENTS

INTRODUCTION

In some ways it is almost too early to do a book on Lionel products made by General Mills. In some ways it is almost too late.

It is almost too early because on some items a clear-cut order of scarcity and demand has not yet been established. Certainly supply has been much more uniform than in the old days. With this lack of a pecking order of availability, ratings are sometimes only educated guesses. The authors have eliminated ratings altogether in some sections. Some of the "what" questions, therefore, that were answered in our other books — What is the rarest? What is the most sought-after? — are not answered in this book. It is too soon.

On the other hand we felt we could wait no longer to get other questions answered, the important "who" and "why" and "when" and "where" questions surrounding corporate decisions, great and small, of both General Mills and Lionel at the beginning of the 1970s. The greatest difficulty we faced in gathering information for our other collectors guides was the lack of primary sources. So much had happened so long before, we often relied on second- and third-hand information. Already, 10 years from the beginning, some pivotal decisions of the new Lionel have become obscured. It would be too risky to wait more than 10 years.

So we went ahead with the project, the last book in our Lionel series. Ten years from now — or 15 for the silver anniversary — someone else can fill in the blanks. What we strove for here, and what we believe we have accomplished, is a thoroughly researched history of the early days and a solid foundation for collectors of General Mills Lionel to build upon.

We did not do it alone, of course. We never do. It is always impossible to thank all the people who helped, but we must acknowledge Bernie Puralewski and Dave Garrigues, experts on so much, who shared their information and made us look smarter than we are. Others who shared their knowledge and time were Howard LeVine, Frank Kloss and John Palm.

Thanks to George Toteff and Dick Branstner and Harry Blum for interviews and repeated phone calls to check and recheck facts; and more phone calls to Lionel Corporation executives Ron Saypol and George Padgett; and more interviews, phone calls, tours and meetings with Fundimensions and Lionel people: Jim Boosales, Bill Diss, John Brady, Pete Sappenfield, Laura Stolicki, Don Billy, Dan Pencak, Chuck Horan, Lenny Dean, Dave Diehm, Dan Johns, Ron Rae, Dick Boss and Del Reickord. Thanks to all for their cooperation and hospitality. Our appreciation also to Paula Dore, who helped in production and to John Merrit, the transportation expert, and Commissioner P. J. Tuohy, the North Woods historian.

All those people helped us make what we hope is, an important contribution to toy train collecting. That's why we did the book, to make a contribution. Well, there *was* another reason. We wanted to do it. We wanted to track down all those executives and former employees, to interview them, to talk about trains, to go through the Lionel plants in Mount Clemens, to look at the archives. We thought it would be fun.

Back in 1973 an enthusiastic but not very experienced train collector was having a hard time running down some specific information about a Lionel train. "Somebody ought to do a book on Lionel," he said. "A guide for collectors, something that would help people who have questions." The collector's name was Tom McComas and he was talking to Jim Tuohy.

"That's a good idea. Why don't *you* do one?" asked Tuohy jokingly. "Why don't *we* do one?" replied McComas, not jokingly. "It might be interesting."

That was the start of it. This, four hardcover books, one softcover book, one movie, and one children's book later, is the end of it. It's been a long ride, sometimes rough. But it has been interesting. It has been fun.

HISTORY

Even before the trains, it was an intrepid enterprise.

It reflected its founder. George Toteff had started the Model Products Corporation, a manufacturer of plastic model kits, in 1962, boldly taking on a giant in the industry, the AMT Corporation of Troy, Michigan. Some had thought he would fail, but the 41-year-old Toteff had seen no reason to be frightened of AMT. He had been, 13 years before, its first employee and was at the time he left its biggest stockholder. By 1968 the sales of Model Products, located in Mount Clemens, Michigan, had surpassed those of AMT and the General Mills Corporation bought his company in a deal that was extremely lucrative for Toteff, who stayed on as president of General Mills's new MPC division.

"George Toteff is the sharpest guy in the hobby business," says a competitor of his. "General Mills," says Toteff in a succinct explanation of why the conglomorate went to MPC when they wanted to acquire a hobby kit company, "is not interested in losers."

The acquisition came in November of 1968, at a time when General Mills was rapidly expanding into the toy field. Within a few months General Mills acquired Parker Brothers, Kenner Toys, Craft-Master (a maker of paint-by-the-numbers kits and a 20 per cent owner of MPC, affiliating Toteff with General Mills before he sold them his own company) and MPC. Watching all of this was a man named Ronald D. Saypol, the president of a firm that had the greatest name in all of toys: The Lionel Corporation of New York, New York.

Lionel had a good name but in 1968 it was making bad trains and it did not even want to make those any longer. Lionel had diversified into the fields of electronics among other things, and was looking for a way to drop its train division. Lionel trains were losing money and anticipated sales for the year 1969 were under $1 million (it turned out to be about $800,000). Saypol contacted Craig A. Nalen, who was a vice-president of General Mills Inc. and General Manager of the Craft, Game and Toy Division. At a meeting soon after, Nalen suggested that George Toteff, who was heading the division's hobbies and crafts, look into the situation.

"I was the natural one because we were in the hobby-oriented end of the business," says Toteff. "Even though the train was a toy, it was as hobby-oriented as it was toy-oriented."

Toteff began to make inquiries. He had never worked in the toy train field but he knew one truth: "At that point the world was not hot for trains." He called a long-time associate, Richard Branstner, a 38-year-old engineer who had worked on and off with Toteff for 20 years. For a time he owned his own business, Branco, which made remote-controlled airplanes. He was, in the words of a fellow executive, "incredibly well-qualified at the engineering and technical side of things."

"Do you think there's a market for toy trains, Dick?" Toteff asked. "Lionel's up for sale."

"I don't know, but it's the best brand name in the country," answered Branstner. "Better than Cadillac, because kids became aware of it during their impressionable years and they never forgot it."

Branstner agreed to go to New Jersey for Toteff and see what Lionel had to sell. He would not return for a year.

Toteff called another colleague, Harry Blum, a marketing specialist who ran a contract manufacturing company with which Toteff did business. Blum's firm, Parkway Manufacturing, made auto racing equipment according to specifications supplied to them by companies like MPC, and would, if a customer desired, arrange a marketing program for them. Blum also made HO and N gauge trains and his father had owned two large hobby stores in Cleveland, dealing in both the wholesale and retail sides of that business. Blum's association with Lionel went back to the days of Joshua Cowen and Arthur Raphael.

"What do you think of Lionel?" Toteff asked him.

"It's still one of the great brand names in existence," answered Blum, who speaks softly and deliberately, carefully shaping each phrase, but with a certain amount of marketing-ese. His manner contrasts sharply with Branstner, who speaks rapidly and in rushes of words.

"What do you think of the train business?" asked Toteff, who also speaks rapidly, but with quiet economy.

"There is an enormous potential in the train business," answered Blum. "As long as you make a decent product, you have an enormous market that the HO people cannot satisfy."

"Well, let's get together and evaluate it," said Toteff. They did and for the next two years Toteff, Blum and Branstner would form an organizational team that would resurrect the Lionel train business. Blum, looking at Lionel's potential from an overall view, felt toy trains could be sold.

"Here are the reasons," says Blum, who is now a motion picture producer. "One, the market you were selling was a market of fathers, all of whom had Lionel trains. Secondly, when I talked to the marketplace I found that the marketplace was not aware of the demise of Lionel. They still looked at Lionel as very viable. The brand name had been that strong. Thirdly, this was a time when the hobby industry was very fragmented — there was no dominant toy. Slot racing had peaked and the slot racing did not have the collector opportunity or the durability and it did not have the father and son identification that trains had. Cars were more of an individual thing.

"I saw what was going on with HO but I realized that HO couldn't satisfy everybody the way it is made. So I felt there was an enormous opportunity to get stability of product, something that all companies strive for but few achieve. General Mills wanted this stability of product. Every toy company wants it." Blum explains stability of product as being the ability to produce the same item — such as train sets — year after year.

"If a toy company doesn't have it they have to come up with a new 'Mr. Machine' every year."

Blum began to evaluate for Toteff exactly where sales of Lionel trains should be directed, provided Dick Branstner found sufficient tooling and personnel at Hillside to put out a line of trains. In March of 1969 Branstner was hard at work at that end of things.

"You would have to signal Branstner as one of the main contributors to the rebirth of Lionel," say Toteff. "Sure, I was spearheading it, but Branstner moved his family to New Jersey and worked out of the old Hillside factory for a year. He gathered around him some of the old Lionel team and just went to work."

The first thing Branstner did was check the Hillside plant to see what sort of shape it was in, to see what it contained and what it didn't.

"I walked into a 30,000-square-foot building filled with old tools and you could hear them saying, 'Use me, use me," Branstner recalls. "Everything was magnificently placed. It was like a museum. None of the top management at Lionel knew what they had. I'm sure Saypol, the president, didn't know how well that place was kept. I've been in Detroit and I know how those big auto companies operate, for instance. If you would have bought Packard or Studebaker, all you get is a hunk of junk. All the Lionel tools were organized and labeled and the same with all the paper work — all the engineering files, engineering books, the standards. Any idiot with half a brain could go in there and do a job with that company if he knew anything about railroads at all."

Branstner met with Lenny Dean, the Lionel service manager and a long-time and very respected Lionel employee. The Hillside plant was operating with only a skeleton crew, but Dean put Branstner in touch with dozens of former employees. Branstner would work in the factory during the day, climbing among boxes heavy with dust, examining and taking notes. At night he would meet with old-line employees, gathering more information.

"I had meetings night after night till 1, 2, 3 o'clock in the morning with old timers. Lenny was a big help, bringing people to me. I would say to a guy, 'Hey, Joe, I'd like to make this locomotive. What do I have to do?' In one hour Joe would give me a complete CPI — Component Parts Index — that showed what tools to use — what the purchase components were, what machinery it took, the plating process, the painting process, and they had a CPI for every item. Finally I saw a pattern."

Representatives from several other companies had looked over the Lionel plant. They did not see what Branstner saw and all had reported negatively to their superiors. One day Lenny Dean talked to Branstner about it.

"They always say it can't be pulled off," said Dean. "They think its just a big white elephant. Do you believe that?"

"No, I don't," answered Branstner. "The longer I stay here the more I think it's duck soup to do."

Branstner's reports to Toteff were growing more and more positive. Toteff made several trips to New Jersey to meet with Branstner and the Lionel people. He would check into a suite at the Irvington Motor Lodge, about a mile from the factory, which straddled the Irvington-Hillside city limits.

"When Toteff came in I would introduce him to some of the old people," says Branstner. "George could do a lot over the phone but he wanted to meet some of the people eye-to-eye and get the feeling I was talking about. We would meet at his rooms at the lodge. Or if he wanted to talk with someone like Joe Bonanno we would go to his home. You don't ask someone like Joe Bonanno to come to you. Toteff thought he was a genius. He is.

"'I would show Toteff all the stuff I had found out. Schedules, blueprints, documents, what tools existed and their condition. I told him it was all there and we had the expertise needed to make a go of it. The expertise was in the old employees; it was unbelievable the loyalty they had to that product. I just felt we couldn't miss. We could make Lionel trains. So Toteff became convinced we could put a quality product on the market. The next thing we had to do was make the deal with Saypol."

The General Mills board of directors also had to be considered. Toteff and Blum were working on that. "Not everyone at General Mills was convinced the Lionel name meant anything," says Blum. "There was a man on the board by the name of F.A.O. Schwarz who was a brilliant attorney and was an expert on toys. He wasn't convinced there was a toy train business. It was our job to convince the board there was."

George Toteff

Schwarz was a member of the New York City toy store family. Once a large customer of Lionel, the store never bought anything but foreign trains after World War II. It appears it objected to the discounting policies adopted by Lionel and other domestic train makers after Fair Trade restrictions were lifted. By 1969, ownership of the store had long since passed out of the Schwarz family's hands. The store had been sold and resold and one of the companies that had considered buying it was Lionel. Whether any of that influenced board director Schwarz's opinion of Lionel is not known, but in spite of his opposition, Toteff and Blum were able to enlist a strong ally in James Summer, who was President and Chief Operating Officer of General Mills and the driving force behind the company's expansion into the toy field.

"With its institutional value, the name 'Lionel' had a lot going for it," says Toteff. "Summer saw the potential. Blum had a lot to do with getting Summer enthusiastic about Lionel. We had a big booster on our team when we had Jim Summer. He was an absolute heavy."

While Blum handled some of the upper echelon lobbying, often working through Craig Nalen, Toteff was negotiating with Lionel's Saypol. During the early months of 1969 they worked out a deal in which General Mills would lease the Lionel name for 10 years, starting in 1970. The arrangement called for Lionel to be paid a royalty of 3 percent of the net sales of all train sets sold during that time, and 5 percent on all "accessories," which were defined as everything other than sets. Lionel would receive a minimum royalty of $50,000 a year — or $500,000 — to be paid in advance. For $65,000, General Mills would purchase the tools, dies, designs, specifications and whatever other special equipment they needed to put out the 1970 line. They had an option to buy all the rest of the tooling and special equipment for $100,000. That option had to be exercised by January 1, 1970, at which time the licensing agreement would go into effect and Lionel would get its cash advance.

Now Toteff had something to go to the General Mills board of directors with. At its April meeting the board approved the acquisition and on April 24, 1969, the deal was signed. On December 31, 1969 the second part of the agreement was signed, giving General Mills outright possession of the rest of the tooling and equipment and Lionel its $665,000. In 1974, when the lease was renegotiated for 10 years, the royalty percentage was changed to a straight 3.5 percent for everything sold, with a prepayment of $1 million, representing a minimum royalty of $200,000 in each of the first five years of the contract. The royalty agreement covers everything General Mills makes with the Lionel name on it, with one exception: car racing. Lionel, being candid in negotiations, said they felt their name had no real value in the car field, which they had entered in the early 1960s and in which they had failed.

"I think the thing that enabled us to convince the board that General Mills should enter the toy train field was the creative deal worked out with Ron Saypol," says Harry Blum. "I think it was to everybody's credit. It was a deal where not a lot of dollars were put together initially but as it has turned out the arrangement with General Mills is a major source of revenue for the Lionel Corporation, and of course, General Mills can well afford it. When you consider there was $30 million in tooling and a brand name of Lionel's stature, there was not the money up-front there would be if you bought the company now. It was a very intelligent deal."

James Boosales is now president of Fundimensions, with overall responsibility for Lionel. At the time of the acquisition he was a 24-year-old assistant in the comptroller's office of General Mills in Minneapolis. He compiled some of the cost figures concerning Lionel that were presented to the board of directors.

"By the time it got to our division and to the guy who was handling acquisition contracts, they had pretty much decided the thing made sense from a marketing standpoint," says Boosales. "Now they wanted figures to justify it from a financial standpoint."

"I think the auditing team they sent in pretty much could look around and say, 'Look, they've got all these tools and they built all these trains — see, they've got all these catalogs — they *must* be worth plenty — and even if they're not the name is worth something by itself.'"

The Lionel Leisure stores, which the Corporation bought from Leonard Wasserman shortly before selling the train operation to General Mills, is now one of the biggest buyers of Lionel trains. This puts Boosales in frequent communication with Lionel President Saypol.

"Ron is happy with the deal," Boosales, a good-natured, curly-haired graduate of Columbia University and the University of Chicago School of Business, says with a quick laugh. "He has seen several presidents of Fundimensions come and go while he just counts the money coming in for doing nothing. And the deal has worked out well for us in the sense that we're making a good business out of this thing."

The principal negotiators, Saypol and Toteff, agree with the general consensus that the deal was mutually beneficial to their companies. They came away with respect for each other.

"Saypol had been in the toy and hobby field prior to diversifying Lionel," says Toteff. "It was a good blend. He was an excellent negotiator, a high-level operator. It was a good deal for everyone."

"The negotiations were tough and good," says Saypol. "He's a straight-dealing, honorable guy and a hard and effective negotiator. I think he did well for his company. They're probably doing as much in dollars as Lionel did in all but three or four years. I'm pleased with the deal. We were not in a position to reactivate the train division and General Mills was. And the product line continues."

Contrary to some reports, Saypol says that he did not contact Revell or any other company about buying Lionel. "General Mill was the first company I contacted. We considered just dropping the trains, but we never really had to make a judgment about it because we did, in fact, end up with the General Mills deal."

Ron Saypol

An interesting footnote to the acquisition was provided by Branstner. "Toteff and I decided that Lionel had such great potential that if General Mills didn't buy it Toteff and myself and some other guys were going to buy it. We felt it was that good."

After General Mills bought Lionel and Dick Branstner's initial research at Hillside was finished, he agreed to stay there and prepare the 1970 line, the first to be made by General Mills. Under the agreement, the Lionel Corporation was responsible for the 1969 line. He became director of engineering and development for Lionel, which became a division of MPC. Blum became general manager in New Jersey.

"We did both a market analysis and a technical analysis," says Blum. "We determined that our initial thrust should be to get back the staple year-to-year business and take advantage of the Lionel name. To do this we felt we had to make a quality product that had the durability to make it a lifetime toy. Secondly, we had to integrate the fun value and the hobby value of the trains, which are the things we know Lionel for."

Branstner, in the meantime, was still plugging away in the Hillside factory, much of the time with his shirtsleeves rolled up and his hands dirty.

"He had gathered his team around him," says Toteff, "and he went into the archives and found some of the old quality pieces and began to study them, those items that once made Lionel the top of the toy industry. The Lionel we brought out in 1970 was not the same Lionel that was produced in 1969, when quality had totally deteriorated."

"In talking with Joe Bonanno and all the old guys from Lionel I got the idea that the quality started to decline somewhere between 1955 and 1959," says Branstner, taking up the narrative. "Somewhere during that time the decision was made to cut costs and cut quality. So in reviewing all the old Lionel I decided to ignore everything made after 1959. I was only interested in what I call the Joe Bonanno Era. He became chief engineer in 1928 and left in 1963. Bonanno convinced me that quality was the only way to go and Toteff agreed. He didn't want any cheapo junk either.

"I began using the archives as much as I used engineering. They were built on to the side of a wall. You wouldn't even know it was the archives. There were big plywood cabinets about three-feet deep. This was up in engineering on the second floor. When you walked through one room to another you would notice that the wall was very thick. One time I asked Lenny Dean what was in there. He said that was where all the engineering samples were kept. So I got this guy from the maintenance department to open the cabinets and there sat all those mint engineering samples going all the way back to the beginning.

Dick Branstner

"You could see the evolution of every product. Every single product was dated and tagged, indicating where the problems were and what was done to correct them; all the information was documented on a little tag that was on each item. What the life expectancy was — everything you needed to know. Then there was another group of stuff locked in cabinets downstairs in the quality control department. Those cabinets had daily production samples going back to 1935 or before."

Gradually Branstner began to formulate in his mind the things he wanted made, not only for 1970 but beyond, tempering desire with the limitations of time and budget. He consulted with Fred Binder of Binder Tool and Mold of Windsor, Canada. Binder and Branstner had worked together on other projects in Michigan. Binder made several trips to the Hillside plant, where he and Branstner would crawl through the storage areas together, pulling tools apart and examining them.

"The first thing we did was sharpen all the tools up," says Branstner. "Binder was the tool expert. He helped streamline all the old tools we were going to use. He'd look at a tool and say, 'Dick, if we do this we can run it faster,' or 'Dick, if we do that we'll get a better part.' He did a super job."

Not all the tooling was in New Jersey, however, and that created a problem for the MPC team. Before Saypol arrived in 1968, Lionel had been run by former president Robert A. Wolfe, a man apparently not held in the highest esteem by Branstner and his co-workers.

"Wolfe had arranged to make part of Lionel engines in Japan," says Harry Blum. "I spent most of my time that first year on the phone with Japan trying to locate tools, molds, dies and all kinds of other stuff that Wolfe sent over there. It was over there under a contract, and the manufacturing was certainly of a lesser quality. There were a lot of problems with quality control. We wanted that stuff back."

They eventually got it, about the time Branstner was setting up the original production lines at New Jersey with some of the old employees, the men whom Branstner relied so heavily upon.

"It was me and Tony Gotto, Jess Marchese, Lou Anzalone," says Branstner. "All ex-Lionel guys. All Italian." He adds jokingly, "If you weren't Italian you couldn't work for Lionel. It was like a big family, almost like a religion, their loyalty to the old product and the old bosses. Joshua Cowen was a god as far as they were concerned.

"The old employees treated the whole '60s thing — when the company was in disarray and the quality of the trains had disintegrated — as a temporary thing that they felt would go away. Lou Anzalone used to build all the old test equipment. The job with Lionel was the only one he ever had in his life. Most of the employees believed the '60s era was just something that had to be put up with until the real Lionel would come back to life.

"Lionel had cut way back and a lot of the old employees were free-lancing, waiting for Lionel to start up again. There was a great pool of talent there."

Branstner has continued to draw from that pool through the years. He is now with Tyco and several of the old Lionel employees, whom he originally brought from New Jersey to Mount Clemens, are with him, including Lou Anzalone.

There have been, incidently, several companies started by Lionel employees who were laid off. Some have started stamping businesses, others molding shops. Jerome Electric of Orange, New Jersey, was started by a man named John DiGirolemo who was the head of the Lionel transformer department. Rapid Tool is owned by Quinnie Qualtier, a Joe Bonanno protege.

The development of the 1970 product line proceeded all during the later part of 1969. Branstner and Blum worked on the catalog together and Blum got the idea for the layout, which was a catalog on one side of a 22-inch-by-34-inch fold-out sheet and a poster on the other.

Harry N. Blum

"The idea of the poster was to show we were doing it differently than before, but nevertheless we still had all those years of tradition to draw upon," says Blum. "The first year we were selling off the past. That first year we were very sensitive about selling a product of satisfactory quality."

To that end Branstner had introduced a few innovations, such as tapered wheels on the rolling stock and needlepoint bearings. Also for the first time the rolling stock wheels were locked to the axles, like real trains. The only time Lionel had done that before was on the scale cars introduced for the 700E Hudson in 1940. Branstner was also busy with graphics.

"My own bag was going out and finding new ways of decorating," Branstner says. "I took the modern techniques of decorating — like electrocal and tampa — and applied them to toy trains. If you look at some of the old Lionel stuff the castings were beautiful but the paint jobs were kind of schlocky. In those days all that was available was rubber stamping for applying graphics.

"I felt it was extremely important to have flashy, handsome graphics. You see, the customer never really sees where the money is spent, because so much of it goes on the inside. Like precision bearings and the ground shafts, that's what he's paying for but he doesn't see it. You have to 'eye-wash' the customer the best way you know how and that's by good decorating — painting and graphics."

In January of 1970 the MPC-Lionel team took their new line — with its fancy graphic techniques, hidden improvements and rush-rush catalog — to the Toy Fair in New York City. They wrote more than $2½ million in orders and went back to New Jersey ready to produce some trains. But suddenly there was a change of plans. The trains would not be made in New Jersey. They would be made in Michigan.

The official explanation for this, given now by the Lionel management team, is simple and sensible, although lacking in detail: it was economically more feasible to make the trains in Michigan, near the MPC home office, than to make them in New Jersey. To a great degree Harry Blum recalls it the same way.

"We had much equipment and manpower already in New Jersey but we had all kinds of obligations at Hillside — overhead costs, union commitments, building agreements — all kinds of continuing obligations that were making us bear the load of the past. During that first year we worked hard to extricate ourselves from those obligations but we finally decided it would work best in Michigan; there were economics in merging the operations, utilizing a going operation rather than starting one from scratch."

Dick Branstner remembers the decision as involving more than just economics, however.

"The production side of the thing wasn't really going the way it should have been. Some of the ways of the old Lionel guy in charge were a little old-fashioned. The production manager and Harry Blum had constant arguments. Toteff realized that the company needed him to guide things directly, not through a chain of command. There's no chain of command with him. If George wants to talk to a floor sweeper, he talks to him and if the floor sweeper has a good idea it's going to be used. The best organizational chart I ever saw was one that a guy once put together for George. It was beautiful. The first thing George did was erase all the lines.

"The people in New Jersey didn't always move at the speed Toteff likes to move, which is like thunder and lightning. He realized he had a big job in resurrecting Lionel and he had Big Brother General Mills looking over his shoulder; he realized he had to put it under his wing and that's what he did. So that was the main reason we moved to Michigan."

The decision was made, in the Toteff manner, firmly and quickly. It was shortly after the Toy Fair when he told Branstner, whose family had just become accustomed to the idea that they were staying in New Jersey indefinitely, that he was going back to Michigan. "I remember going home and telling my wife. She jumped four feet off the floor."

Now came the enormous job of moving to Michigan. The orders at the Toy Fair had been taken in the belief that the trains would be made at Hillside and that production would start almost immediately. Now, whatever production schedule there was had to be abandoned, the tooling moved to Mount Clemens, and production equipment reassembled. Toteff would take care of finding a plant, and Branstner would oversee the move and the production set-up in Mount Clemens. Blum would stay in New Jersey, where it was decided that a few items would still be made.

"We kept a little production in New Jersey because we wanted to keep in touch with the talent there, those who would not move or commute," Says Toteff. "I knew there was still a lot of brainpower there, even though Dick had gotten some of the key people to move. But in Michigan I had some of the founders of the hobby industry with me. We had excellent mold makers, excellent molders, excellent engineers and excellent model makers. I had 50 or 60 key people at MPC. So we tried to supplement that team with the people we had from Lionel. At MPC we had a great model shop and a complete art and engineering department."

Toteff rented an old Ford paint plant on 23-Mile Road in Mount Clemens and in February of 1970 the move began. Twenty semi-trailers were loaded with tooling, assembling equipment and track machines. Only the tooling needed to produce the 1970 line was moved at this time. Another, smaller move was completed later in the year when the archives and some other things were shipped to Mount Clemens. The remaining tooling was moved two years later. Branstner's heaviest work load began in April of 1970, when he began to set up the production line, and continued through the spring and summer as he got out the new line.

"I had five or six guys flying in every week from New Jersey to help me set up that production line in Mount Clemens," says Branstner. "I made a deal with the best guys from old Lionel I could get my hands on. I would fly them to Michigan every Sunday night and fly them back to New Jersey on Saturday, or maybe not at all. I got them to work right through. Everyone worked around the clock. If we got two hours sleep a night for two months it was a lot. Lionel had terrific people.

I got two of them to move to Michigan permanently. One was Howard Steinberg and the other was Lou Anzalone. They are both still with me. There was a top-notch guy, Bill Felich, who left to start his own business. I would have thrown myself on the floor to stop him. They should have offered him a contract. You have to keep the good people."

It was a hectic spring and summer, that time in 1970, as the Lionel team struggled to get the new line in the stores by Christmas. At one point the lamination die for the transformer was lost.

"We shipped it to Stampings Inc. in Mount Clemens. They were going to use it to make parts for us," Branstner recalls. "A week later in a meeting with the purchasing department, they want to know where the stamping die for the transformers is. I tell them it was shipped to Stampings Inc.

"They call Stampings Inc. and Stampings Inc. says they don't have it. So everybody starts looking for it. The thing is two-feet square and is a solid block of carbide steel. It has to weigh almost two tons. But it's vanished. You're talking about a tool that cost $30,000 and takes six months to build. We want to deliver train sets by Christmas and the one key item to make a transformer is missing. I mean this thing seemed to have gone off the face of the earth. We checked everywhere.

"So here we are at another meeting and we're wringing our hands over the missing die. Then one guy asks if anyone has thought of calling the lost and found. At that everybody starts busting a gut laughing. The lost and found? What lost and found? The state of Michigan. So we have the guy call. We make the same guy who's dumb enough to ask the question be the jerk that has to make the call.

" 'We're missing a die,' he says to the cop. 'What's it look like?' the cop asks. 'It's 24-inches square and weighs about two tons,' our guy says. 'Does it have a number on it?' asks the cop. Our guy tells him the number. Their guy says, 'Hey, Lou, what's the number on that thing? . . . Yeah, we got it.'

"What happened was the truck was taking it from the Lionel plant to Stampings Inc. on a flat bed and it wasn't tied down secure enough. The truck turned a corner and the die fell off and rolled down into a 12-foot deep ravine. The cops got a big winch truck, pulled it out and hauled it to the state lost and found. Since then, whenever anything is missing we ask, 'Did anyone call the lost and found?' "

Losing dies was not without precedent in Lionel's history, as Branstner had earlier discovered. Lionel and other toy train companies often disposed of obsolete dies. They usually did not destroy them themselves but sold them as scrap. During the war years, both World War II and Korea, there were drives by the government to collect scrap and Lionel contributed some obsolete dies. During the Korean War Lionel gave a number of Bakelite dies to the war effort. Unfortunately, counter to the specific orders of Joe Bonanno, the Bakelite dies for the Irvington cars were given away. It was a mistake that was a matter of great frustration for Branstner.

Even more frustrating for everyone — from the early Lionel-General Mills team to the present management — is the disappearance of irreplacable samples from the archives. Much was stolen in New Jersey after the original move of the tooling and assembly equipment. Still more was stolen in the intermediate years in Mount Clemens.

"It was never cataloged or secured properly after it got to Michigan," says Branstner. "I tried to tell them those archives were priceless. The move of the archives should have been handled by a Pinkerton team because once the stuff is gone that's the end of it. I don't know how the archives are today but I know when I left the company in 1975 the archives were a pathetic case."

The archives were still disorganized in 1979 but at least top management had become aware of their value and the need for tight security to protect them.

"Those archives were ripped off a lot," says Fundimensions President Jim Boosales. "They're secure now but prior to the last two years they were hit by a lot of people in the company. A lot of people, too many, had access to them. We know it happened. What they took was mostly production run samples of old stuff. You put that out at a meet somewhere and it's gone and nobody can trace it. If they took prototype stuff, that's a little easier to track down.

"At one point we found out we had only one set of the old aluminum cars. That was when we were preparing to re-issue them. We had to move them back and forth and back and forth as proto-types. It was that or buy some from collectors. At a dealer show in Chicago in early 1979 we had to show a borrowed Williams car as an example of the aluminum car we were coming out with. The one set we had got hung up in Michigan during the big snow storm."

Jim Boosales

Boosales has placed one of his most com-petent executives in charge of the archives. He is William Diss, the manager of Fundimensions administrative services.

"There are a lot of things in private collec-tions now that came out of our archives," says Diss. "We had a complete collection of cata-logs that were in an unlocked filing cabinet. Just sitting there, accessible to all our produc-tion people. The catalogs vanished. We have pictures of a lot of stuff that was in the archives that I know has been stolen. The stuff is just not there any more."

In spite of the uncertainty of moving, the shuffling of equipment, the theft of the archives and the diversion of a two-ton die to the Michigan State Police Lost and Found, the 1970 line was delivered to the stores in time for the Christmas season. The main emphasis of the line was on sets and 100,000 of them were sold.

The catalog was rather grandiose in its claims: some of what was offered was not actually produced. But the Lionel team essen-tially achieved what they had striven for. They got the line out and it was a distinct improve-ment over 1969.

"We did that fancy catalog because we knew we weren't going to have a big line," says Harry Blum. "We wanted to make a small line and make sure everything we made was good. We had gone through — or at least the Lionel name had gone through — a few years in which what was sold was so inconsistent with what people knew the name to represent that we had to change that. To guarantee that we change it, to exercise maximum quality control, we had

to limit the amount we produced. We had to bring Lionel's quality up to a level that the name implied or we weren't going to have a successful company."

Lionel in the first year was known as a division of MPC, but other than George Toteff, who oversaw the model kit aspect of MPC, too, the Lionel group always considered themselves a separate operation from MPC, although they did share administrative offices in the MPC building on Groesbeck Road in Mount Clemens, a few miles from the Lionel plant on 23-Mile Road. As the planning for the 1971 line progressed, Lionel's administrative staff moved to a two-story red brick building on 23-Mile Road, just down the road from the plant.

With the physical separation of the Lionel and MPC offices, Lionel began to function even more pronouncedly as a separate division of General Mills. The Lionel boxes and catalogs continued to refer to Lionel as a "Division of MPC" but that was misleading. All during the early 1970s Model Products concentrated ex-clusively on its kits and Lionel concentrated strictly on its trains, even though the trains carried the MPC logo. Then, in 1975, the separation became official when General Mills established an umbrella group called Fundi-mensions.

Under the Fundimensions heading came three separate and equal divisions: Lionel, MPC and Craft-Master. Each division has it own products manager and marketing manager. The products manager concerns himself with the nuts and bolts of the day-to-day operation and setting up the line; the marketing manager concerns himself with sales, promotion and public liaison. Both report to the president of Fundimensions, who since 1977 has been Jim Boosales. The current marketing manager at Lionel is C. R. Sappenfield, while John Brady, the assistant products manager, has been func-tioning as products manager, although he is scheduled to move to another division by the end of 1979. There are several different vice-presidents of Fundimensions and their responsi-bilities are to all three companies. The engi-neering department also works on all three lines, as does the art department and the con-sumer relations department, which is now headed by former Lionel marketing manager Dan Johns.

After that scrambling inaugural year of 1970, the Lionel line expanded every year. Sales increased, too, jumping sharply in 1973, when many new items were offered. One item that was pictured in the catalog in 1973 but was never offered to the general public was Trutrack. It was cataloged again in 1974 but again was not sold. Some straight and curved sections were made and distributed to service stations but the switches never were. Trutrack was a realistic-looking item with a narrow middle rail, eight cross ties to a section, and a wide-turning radius (somewhere between O and 072). It also had a snap-on road bed. The company said trouble with the switching section of the track, made in Italy to Lionel specifications, kept the item from meeting Lionel standards. Dick Branstner has a different opinion.

"I think the real reason it failed was because it didn't have company support. We had the technical problems worked out. It was good looking but it was very expensive and the whole marketing philosophy at Lionel regarding track has always been to sell expensive train sets and 30 cents worth of track. This new track would have cost five times what standard track would have cost. Track doesn't mean anything to anybody. It's like the road you drive on with your car. It's the same road whether you're driving a Cadillac or a Model A."

The Lionel plant was enlarged over the years and eventually a second plant, down the road from the first, was opened. By 1976, the entire MPC operation, production and office, had moved out to 23-Mile Road, sharing with Lionel 50,000 square feet of office space and 370,000 square feet of plant space. By that time, the original team that had spearheaded the takeover of the old Lionel had also moved on.

The first to go was Harry Blum, who acted as Toteff's general manager in New Jersey until he left in the spring of 1971. "My responsibility was to research the market and establish some programs," says Blum. "We evaluated everything on the market everywhere in the world. We investigated many aspects of scale trains. I did my job in the two years. It was harrowing but I look at my time at Lionel with pride. We brought a baby back to life."

George Toteff, who now is president of Craft House, a competitor of Craft-Master, left MPC in early 1973 but remained as a consultant and then returned in July of 1973 as acting general manager until March of 1974, when he brought in Ted Betker, who became

president. Toteff once again became a consultant, during which time the new percentage deal with Lionel was worked out, and then left for good in July of 1974.

Branstner left in 1975, when he was given a one-year contract as a consultant. He has rather bad feelings about the end of his term of service at Lionel.

"They started going cheap," he says. "Plastic motor housings, slider collector shoes rather than roller collector shoes, plastic wheels on the loco. That's not Lionel. This was about '74 and '75. We wanted to get into more of the old stuff and make it with new tooling. I wanted to get into more play value by coming out with new accessories so the kids' attention span would last longer. Revive the excitement. But all you would hear was 'Make it cheaper, make it cheaper!' They felt the way to go was to the mass market with cheap trains. They all but ignored the collectors. When collectors came in to talk with these guys they wouldn't even give them the time of day. It was kind of a sad thing.

"We had to eliminate the paint on some locos, cut back on some decoration, leave some cars and track out of sets, go to a small 12-watt transformer. Things like that Toteff and I hated to do. Back in '70 even our low-end stuff had good motors. That's why I left with a bad taste in my mouth. They put me out to pasture for a year so I wouldn't go with competition; they gave me a nice contract and used me as a consultant. Then management changed again and I was glad to get out of there."

Whatever the justification of Branstner's remarks (and there were complaints for a time by collectors that they weren't being heeded), it was perhaps inevitable that men like George Toteff and Dick Branstner would leave a large corporate structure like General Mills. The fascination, the fun, was in the original challenge: revive Lionel. But once that was accomplished, the day-in and day-out administrative details of dealing along an involved corporate ladder would lead to tedium, frustration and finally disaffection.

Bill Diss, the present Fundimensions administrative service manager — which is the administrative end of engineering for all three companies — was in the Lionel engineering department when Branstner was vice-president of engineering and development.

"He was a very creative person and he was a very good engineer," says Diss. "But he wasn't a very good administrative type. Unfortunately, he was required to do a lot of paper work and he wasn't very good at paper work. He also had to talk with our higher echelon corporate people and he wasn't quite as polished as the average vice-president."

Branstner himself doesn't entirely disagree with that assessment. "The really hard years, the really good years, were between 1969 and 1974. We worked our tails off. Then it got bogged down and I got a little like George Toteff. Sometimes Toteff doesn't know when to keep his mouth shut because his morals mean more to him than money. Plus it doesn't affect him financially; he's got a lot of money, so what does he care? I got to be like George. Very independent. But I couldn't afford it."

After Branstner left, Sam Bushala, who had started in the engineering department in the beginning of the new Lionel, became vice-president of engineering and marketing. In 1974 a man named William Hawfield took over as products manager and began to pay close attention to some things that had previously been neglected, including the opinions of collectors. Hawfield joined several collectors' clubs and made himself available for seminars and for informal interviews at various shows. Some of what Hawfield absorbed from collectors around the country began to show itself in various resurrected items of the mid-'70s.

Hawfield, a rising General Mills executive, was promoted in 1976 and is now president of General Mill's coin and stamp collecting division, H. E. Harris. His departure from Lionel, which saddened many collectors, points to a continuing problem. The present

C. R. "Pete" Sappenfield

Lionel management team, from Boosales down through men like Pete Sappenfield, Bill Diss, and assistant products manager John Brady, seem to have a genuine interest in making the best trains they can, given certain budgetary limitations, and to have a sense of the historical significance of the Lionel name. But Brady is already scheduled to leave and any of the others could abruptly depart, if for no other reason than their own competence and desire for advancement. Lionel executives acknowledge this has been a problem in the past but Boosales thinks experience and intelligent long-range planning can create a consistency of product and customer relations that can transcend shifts in management.

One person who has been with Lionel from the start is consumer relations director Daniel Johns. He started as a draftsman with MPC in 1968 and has held a variety of positions, including products manager and marketing manager. In his present job, Johns handles 30,000 letters a year from Lionel customers. Those from collectors and others making suggestions on what items Lionel should make are turned over to the products manager. If it was once true that collectors were ignored, it is not true any more. John Brady has stacks of letters in his office.

"We read the letters as they come in," he says. "Then we sort them. The letters making suggestions on what items to resurrect are placed in stacks according to the item suggested. When a certain stack gets big enough we start paying attention."

Lionel estimates that 40 to 50 percent of its business is to collectors, but on higher priced items such as the FM or the GG-1 they estimate 95 percent of the pieces go to collectors.

"More and more the line is being drawn between the collector and the mass market," says John Brady. "The collector will move down occasionally, but not often. We are hoping we can get some of the mass market to move up. We hope the Chesapeake Flyer is an item a new buyer can build on, and perhaps become a collector."

There are those, some collectors included, who believe separating the mass market from the collector's market is the wrong way to go about things, that more attention should be paid to improving the line from the bottom up and let the general market place determine what will eventually become collectors items. They would eliminate limited editions, among other things. One who thinks that way is Dick Branstner, who is a collector himself.

"The collector stuff should come out of your prime market, which is your mass market. That's the way it was in the beginning. There was no distinction between collectors and mass market. If they made things for the mass market they would make more and prices would come down. The only reason they are in the collector business is because they have the old tools. What are they going to do when that stuff wears out?"

It should be pointed out that Branstner is now with Tyco, a firm not known for its high quality mass market items.

In the first days of the new Lionel, it was Branstner and the engineering department who selected what items would be made. Branstner, in the days before there was a marketing department, simply figured out what he wanted to make, what road name or brand name to give it, and went ahead and had a prototype made.

Today the decision on what items will be produced is a little more involved than that, but it is still relatively uncomplicated.

"Pete Sappenfield might get an idea," says Brady. "He might kick it around with me and Bill Diss. Then we will take the idea to Engineering and Development and say, 'We'd like to put this item out for $150. What do you think?' They study it and come back with an answer. If it's feasible we'll go on from there. If it's not, it will probably get scrapped."

Eventually, by studying a computerized record of past sales, the marketing department will decide on a skeleton line for the upcoming year. They go to Bill Diss.

Bill Diss

"They will say, 'O.k., we want to do four new SD-18s, eight new boxcars, four tankers' and so on," says Diss. "John Brady and I will go to the files and look through pictures. We'll pick the road names or brand names we want made into prototypes. The main consideration is looks. What's colorful and looks good, especially on the Famous Name boxcar series. The fact that nobody has heard of a particular road name is not that important. If the graphics look good the piece will sell. You will see a lot more smaller lines in the future and less recognizable road names. Most have been used

so many times our customers are getting tired of seeing them. But, of course, the big roads are constantly changing their graphics, so if they develop a brand new catchy color scheme we will probably use it."

The files Diss referred to, the ones he and Brady look through in selecting road names, are kept in Diss's office and contain thousands of pictures of engines and rolling stock. Diss and his staff of three write to every railroad in the United States with more than 14 miles of track. They request color photographs of at least one type of engine, boxcar and caboose.

"Most roads send back at least one of the items requested," Diss says. "Railroads like the Santa Fe and Union Pacific, which are very cooperative, send us everything we ask for. Smaller railroads won't but most send something. I also get all the different railroad magazines and have an extensive library of railroading books. *Extra 2000 South,* which is a diesel spotting railfan magazine, is one I use extensively. They take all their photos in black and white but they usually give an explanation of the color underneath. If I am interested from what I've read, I will write the line and request color photos and color chips."

The decision to resurrect an item usually comes after much mulling over by Diss, who checks with Brady on how the collector mail is going, pages through old Lionel catalogs, listens to ideas from colleagues, absorbs marketing reports on sales, and meanders through the archives, waiting for something to strike his fancy. If an idea gets to the discussion stage, Diss or somebody else will walk out to plant No. 1 and see if the tools for the potential item are there. If they are, further discussions can proceed, including a check with the accounting department to see if the cost of tooling would be justified by potential sales. If the die is not there — and they have been known to be missing — the idea is almost assuredly dropped. Lionel has so far shown no interest in having new dies cast for old items.

During the summer of 1979, while Diss and Brady were selecting the road names for the 1980 line, some of the items from the archives sitting on a table in Diss's office were a 54 ballast tamper, 53 Rio Grande snow plow, 60 trolley, 352 icing station, 3435 aquarium car, 464 lumber mill, 192 control tower, and an American Flyer barrel loader. All or any of them might be produced some day.

"I'm quite impressed with the Flyer accessory," says Diss. "That thing will run forever."

After it is decided that an item will be produced, a prototype is made by the art department. First Diss and Brady pick the colors they want the piece painted. Someone from the art department air brushes the requested color. If it is a shade he doesn't have, he just mixes what he has available until he gets the correct

John Brady

shade and then he tells the paint department how he mixed it so they can duplicate it for the production run.

Once the piece is painted, Dave Diehm, who heads the art department, will sketch a rough design and turn it over to one of the artists, who makes a finished design on mylar, a plastic transparency from which a dry transfer is made. This dry transfer is called a "rubdown" by the Lionel people and it is applied to the car by simply rubbing the back of it with the top of a pen or anything else that's handy. Sometimes, if there is a great rush to get the prototype photographed for a catalog, a logo will be made more simply. They just cut pieces out from an actual label and paste them onto the car. The photograph is then re-touched.

Prototypes that were rushed through are quite easily identified as prototypes, but most of the prototypes made now are so close to the production model that it is extremely hard to tell the difference. Sometimes the only difference is that a "rubdown" is used on the prototype and a heat-stamp or electrocal process is used on the production run.

"Sometimes we destroy the prototype so it doesn't somehow get mixed up with the regular production models," says Diss.

"Destroying prototypes becomes a matter of fairness," says Boosales. "It's really better not to take a chance on letting it get out and have someone make a lot of money on it. That's not fair to everyone else. We've even been thinking of having auctions of prototypes at train club conventions. The money would go to some charity."

The people at Lionel have become extremely security conscious, for they know how valuable even their scrap has become. "We have people going through our dumpsters here," says Boosales. "A guy almost got crushed because he was crawling around in the trash. We put security gates around it now and we sort everything. Nothing leaves that plant unless it is shredded. I mean everything with the Lionel name on it is shredded."

When it comes to getting permission to use the logo of a railroad or a brand name, the companies are almost uniformly cooperative. The process of selecting a brand name is almost identical to the process used in selecting a railroad name. Diss goes through the Thomas Register of businesses in the country. "When we decided to do the soda pop reefers I looked under 'Beverage Companies.' When we did the beer series I looked under 'Breweries.' We sent them a letter saying we planned to do a series of cars in their product area and asked them if they would send their current logo and graphics. The same process was followed for the candy companies and all the others. When we select one to use, they usually give us permission. They know we put out a quality product. They get all kinds of exposure and it doesn't cost them anything. It's a good p.r. tool for them."

Occasionally a company will ask for a royalty but Lionel does not pay royalties. "If someone asks for one we turn it over to Bill Woodlock, the vice-president for personnel," says John Brady. "He's a lawyer and he explains things to them. If they still want a royalty we find another brand." Back in 1973, when Lionel was considering doing the 9850 Budweiser billboard reefer, Budweiser said it wanted a royalty. Dick Branstner called August Busch, the owner of the brewery. "Look, Augie," Branister said, direct as always, "we're as big a name as you are. We can do you a lot of good. What do you need a royalty for?" Busch relented.

Sometimes a company, for its own private reasons, does not want its logo used on a Lionel car, royalty or no royalty. Such was the case of the Kraft Philadelphia Cream Cheese reefer, which was pictured in the 1979 Fundimensions corporate catalog but was never produced. The prototype had already been made when Kraft sent word that they didn't want their logo used. Lionel made the Hills Brothers coffee reefer instead.

If an item requires some new tooling to manufacture, such as the adjustment on the dies to make an SD-18 cab from a GP-7 cab, it takes about a year from the time the decision to make it is made to the time it moves off the production line. If an item, such as a billboard reefer, requires no new tooling but merely new graphics and paint, it can be ready for boxing much faster, within two months perhaps, depending on production schedules of other items. The amount of each item produced is determined by the orders received for it at the Toy Fair held in New York each January.

The subject of numbers is a touchy one with the Lionel management. "By releasing figures on the number of cars we make," says Brady, "we're determining what the secondary market value is, what the resale value is, which we don't want to have anything to do with. We also don't want the competition to know what we're doing."

The question that immediately arises is. What competition? A. C. Gilbert, the maker of American Flyer, went bankrupt in 1966 when Lionel purchased their train tooling, and Ives in 1928. There's nobody left in O gauge.

"We consider we're in competition with the reproduction people such as Williams, the HO toy trains, and with ourselves, our old stuff," according to Brady. "Before we produce an item we take into consideration how plentiful it is on the collectors market. For instance, we did not think the F-3 Santa Fe would sell as well as it did because it was such a common item in the '50s and '60s. We were wrong about that but it's still a consideration."

"I have a problem with letting out production figures," says Boosales. "Part of the problem is that I have never had anyone explain to me whether it's better to let the numbers out or not to let them out. I just don't have a clear understanding.

"See, I've never worked in a business before where the number you make is important. Auto companies let the figures out. I'm still trying to make a final decision on whether or not to release numbers."

There has been some confusion among collectors over the term "Limited Edition," which is a one-run item or, as Brady says, "our pledge that we will never make more of that item." Some collectors assume a limited run item is less than a regular run, but that is not necessarily true. A Limited Edition run may actually be more than a regularly cataloged item. It depends on advance orders. Lionel will make as many of a Limited Edition as it thinks it can sell. It just will not make a re-run. If it doesn't sell all a Limited Edition the first year, it will be cataloged until it is sold out. Boosales says, however, that the Limited Editions in his time have all come out around the same figure.

"I can assure you that the limited production runs that we've made since I've been here have all been very tight around 6,000. On the Penn Central some people thought we made more than 6,000. We didn't. We made the same amount of the Penn Central as we did the Pennsy, within a few pieces."

Boosales referred to speculation among collectors that more of the 8850 Penn Central GG-1s were made in 1978 than 8753 Pennsylvania five-stripers had the previous year. There appeared to be more Penn Centrals around because they didn't sell as well as anticipated.

"We have some left," says Boosales," and we'll keep it in the catalog until it's gone."

Lionel sales have been down for the last two years but Boosales is optimistic about the future, even though he frankly acknowledges the special problems built into the toy train business.

"Lionel has never been especially profitable for General Mills," he says. "There are collectors out there who yell about prices who would not believe that. But Lionel requires a high investment, not just in terms of people and machines and that huge plant and tools, but in terms of inventory. We have many parts that go into each unit, and because there are so many parts involved, and some of them are complicated parts, you have to order way ahead of time and then you end up holding inventories. All this costs money. And when you have the final product finished, you end up inventoring that, too. We'll turn our inventories less than two times in a year. But I'll turn inventory four or five times with my other businesses. In addition, we give dating (allowing more time to pay) to a lot of Lionel customers, so our receivables are high.

"Now, when you are figuring a return on your investment, you have to figure it against your capital, receivables and inventory dollars. On that basis this turns out not to be a very profitable business — based on the return for your investment.

"That's our problem and we are wrestling with it. Part of it is just cleaning up that plant. We have done an awful lot of work paring down those inventories, cleaning things out, starting to identify everything we have.

"But when I say this is not really a profitable business, like say, the pharmaceutical business where they just rake in profit hand over fist, it is not to say it is not a business worth being in. Toys and hobbies are a basic part of General Mills business and you just do not walk away from it. Lionel is carrying a lot of overhead. The key from General Mill's standpoint is to increase sales volume. Get more things being run through our plants. That will help profitability. I can see why Lionel went out of business; they had nothing else going through the New Jersey plant and they were saddled with work rules and union problems that were much more complex than we have.

"The Lionel Corporation has collected $4 million from us over the last 10 years, but I would still rather be on our side than theirs. I know their side. They're one of our biggest customers. I can make a lot more money keeping Lionel here in the long run than the royalties I pay those guys. Things are straightening up. There are two ways to measure a business. One is by the bottom line; the other is by sales. Our sales are down for the second year in a row, but our bottom line is better."

For the immediate future Boosales sees the increased use of DC, or Direct Current, and the reintroduction of the HO line, which failed in 1974 and 1975. "The control systems we are working on right now are very important to Lionel's future," he says. "The control systems may be the biggest reason to buy Lionel, whether it's O gauge or HO."

Until 1979 only the bottom-of-the-line sets were equipped with DC and some Lionel executives, including Bill Diss, fear that collectors have come to think of it as an inferior product. The big advantage in converting to DC is that it is cheaper to make. To reverse a DC motor all you do is reverse polarity. That eliminates the need for the expensive E-unit. A DC motor is also smaller and could fit into accessories. It would give more flexibility to the entire line.

The disadvantages of the DC system are that the horns and whistles would have to be disconnected, and that after a certain amount of time the E-units become magnetized and the engine will eventually stop running. The horns

and whistles presently work on a DC energizer and they would blare all the time on DC if not disconnected.

"A few things have to be worked out about the horn and E-unit but we will work them out," says Boosales. "And we will always have the AC motors in the heavy-duty collector things because we can charge collectors the price required to make an AC motor. But when you get in the mass market area, making hand-wound motors in this day and age is out of the question.

"Although we won't change the motors on our collector line, we may provide a sophisticated DC power pack that can run an engine like the FM. Therefore, we can slowly develop a compatible system. The only person left in the lurch is the person who buys some of our DC units and wants to run them off his AC transformer. But for him we will be selling a little converter — for a dollar — that will convert his AC transformer to DC and he can run his system DC.

"As far as HO is concerned, we might have that on the market as early as 1981. I think in the mass market area the set buyer will go for either O or HO, depending on what strikes him. Both gauges are competing for his dollar. The problem they had the first time around with HO was assuming the Lionel name would sell it. The Lionel name is important but it doesn't help you get a higher price for goods that are not easily differentiated. This time we hope to combine the Lionel name with some exciting new concepts — especially in electronics — and gain public acceptance. You can't live on the name alone in the mass market."

While Lionel's DC-powered HO gauge will run on two-rail track, its DC-powered O gauge will continue to run on three-rail track, which is more efficient. "No matter what, we're sticking with three-rail track," says marketing manager Pete Sappenfield.

One item Lionel decided not to stick with was a remote controlled train, called the Radio Control Express, which was pictured in the 1979 corporate catalog but was never put into production. Lionel had planned a big TV advertising campaign for the RC train, as it was called, but they scrapped their plans.

"We had targeted the RC train at kids, at the mass market," says Boosales, "but when we got into play testing, even though we were pretty far down the development cycle, we realized the train did not provide enough freedom, enough flexibility. It really was just a train on a track. You could walk around with this portable radio and transmit a signal to a battery powered train and make it go back and forth and change speed and that was it. The cheapest train made does that and has been doing that since about 1900.

"Trains pose an interesting dilemma. They were the first things to be minaturized and remotely controlled. By the nature of the way a train operates on a track, it can be realistically powered and controlled. In all these years they've never been able to do that with anything else very effectively until recently. Now with electronics, with radio control, we can still control things but the operator can have much freedom.

"That's what we're working on now, on control systems that provide more realism than have been provided in the past, and that get into more sophisticated controls, more sophisticated sounds, more sophisticated action for the mass market.

"For the collector, which I think breaks down to about 50 per cent of our business, anything we do is going to involve new tooling. We are doing a lot of analysis right now to determine what is the best way to go. If we design completely new trains like the turbo, they will not be designed like the old trains. They will have to have DC power. They will have to have more economical, streamlined components.

"The cost of tooling is almost prohibitive today, but even with the high cost we are analyzing whether we could make a new engine just for the collector market. I think it cost us $110,000 to restore the tools to make the SD-18. Just for the new trucks and to slightly change the GP-7 body.

"We have to be careful not to oversupply the collector market. There is just so much that can be absorbed. We can't retain the same market indefinitely. It has to be sustained from the mass market. It is important that we somehow get kids interested in trains again. It's important to the operators and collectors in the long term because those who get interested in trains as kids tend to be the most avid enthusiasts later on. Kids today are the key to keeping the whole thing going.

"I determine how the Fundimensions money is going to be allocated among Lionel, MPC and Craft-Master. General Mills has always found it difficult to come up with money for capital expenditures such as new tooling. But it may be that the collector stuff will warrant more dollars. My new boss (Bernard Loomis, group vice-president of the Creative Products Group) used to be president of Kenner. He comes out of the toy business and understands that you have to spend money to make money."

It is obvious that Lionel will be trying to capture more of the mass toy market in the near future. That brings the promise of great accomplishments but it also brings the possibility of difficulty and trouble. But there have been difficulty and trouble before. There was trouble in 1910 when Ives decided to make electric trains and Joshua Cowen tried to sell out; there was trouble in 1934 when the company was in receivership; there was trouble in the 1940s when there was a war and in the '50s when they overlooked the HO market and in the '60s when they overlooked the whole train market and almost went under again.

But there were always good people to get them through the trouble: Joshua Cowen himself and Mario Caruso and Arthur Raphael and Phillip Marfuggi and Joe Bonanno and Lenny Dean and, at the beginning of the new Lionel, George Toteff and Dick Branstner. They all gave a little more than they had to.

"I went to New Jersey and started working with those Lionel people and after six months I got to feel it was my baby," says Branstner. "They left an orphan sit there and it was up to me to care for it. I loved what I did. I'd do it again tomorrow if somebody would ask me and I'd do it for nothing. That's how great it was."

When Ronald Saypol took over as president of the Lionel Corporation in 1968 he immediately set about selling the train division, which had lost $13 million in 10 years.

"It wasn't as cold a decision as some people think," says one of the officers of the Lionel Corporation who was there at the time. "He was distressed by what had become of the trains. He had previously worked there for 10 years and was the former son-in-law of Cowen's daughter. But the corporation did not have the money to do what had to be done to save the company. Ron made it a point not to sell to anyone he felt would not care about doing a good job or have the money to do it properly. He sought out General Mills because he thought it was a blue chip company. His prime objective was to sell it to the right people."

It looks very much as if he did.

FACTORY

The headquarters of Fundimensions is a two-story, red-brick building that lies just beyond the Grand Trunk Railroad tracks on 23-Mile Road, seven miles to the north of downtown Mount Clemens, Michigan.

The building is snug against a low treeless hill so that from 23-Mile Road it appears to be only one-story high. Its nearest neighbors are a blue and white Ford paint plant a quarter of a mile to the east and a large industrial park the same distance to the west. In the industrial park, on Richard W. Road, are two flat, indistinctive buildings made of brick, concrete and metal. These are called Plant 1 and Plant 2 by the Fundimensions people and are where Lionel trains are made.

Plant 1 has 125,000-square feet of space and once was a Ford paint plant, too. In 1970, when it was decided to move Lionel's tooling and assembly equipment from New Jersey to Mount Clemens, General Mills rented the old Ford plant. That was the only place in Mount Clemens where Lionel was made until 1976, when Plant 2, with 245,000-square feet of space, was rented. Now both Lionel and MPC share space in the two plants. Since 1976 they have also shared space in the red brick administrative building down the road. Before that, the MPC offices were in the same building as the old MPC plant, which was three miles away on Groesbeck Road.

The third division of Fundimensions, Craft-Master, has offices and its entire manufacturing facility in Toledo, Ohio.

Plant 1 is where motors, transformers, and track are made and engines, accessories and miscellaneous items assembled. It also holds the customer service and replacement parts departments.

Plant 2 is where the molding, decorating and painting are done and all rolling stock other than engines are assembled.

In Plant 1, in a corner near the front door, there is a sub-assembly area where smaller parts of the motor are put together, such as contact bars onto plastic roller housings or axles onto wheels.

In a nearby area the motor itself is assembled and tested. The motor, with the driving wheels attached, is run for 60 to 90 seconds to break it in, half of that time forward and half backward. First it is run at high speed to eliminate burrs on the shaft. Then it is run on low voltage to make sure it functions correctly. The high speed can overcome a malfunction, but the low voltage will expose the fact that something is not working. Then the motor is placed on a short keyhole-shaped section of test track. A weight, equal to that of a cab and a load, is placed on the motor and it is run up a grade, around a curve and down again. There are voltage and time specifications for each type of motor. If it does not make it up the grade within its specifications, the motor is rejected and examined again.

Nearby, armatures are wired and the E-units are assembled and tested. One worker sits at a station with two testing machines, each of which can hold four E-units at one time. The E-units are plugged in and if they are fuctioning correctly a light goes on.

Adjacent to the sub-assembly and testing areas are the cabbing lines. Here the motor, body and E-units come together for assembly. At the end of the line is the testing station for the completed engine. It is run forward, backward and around a curve to make sure it is not binding. Then it is run up a 30-degree grade on 10 sections of straight track. Once again, according to the specifications of each type of engine, a light and a bell at the top of the ramp will go off if the engine is too slow. The rejected engines are then inspected and fixed. On the average about one out of ten fail to make it up the ramp in time.

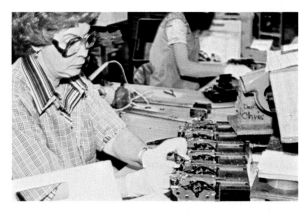

Testing motors.

Track on which motors without cabs are run.

Alco climbs grade on final testing run.

Engines which complete testing are packaged.

Every engine is tested, but not life-tested. There is, under the archives in the engineering department, a life-testing room. There, an engine is weighted to simulate various loads and it is run until it dies or until it reaches 100 hours, which is about the maximum number of hours a child can be expected to play with a train in his life. The engine can run longer, but normally in the life-testing room they don't bother to run it any longer. The testing is done on a computer, which automatically records when an engine stops. If it stops for a simple malfunction like a wheel jumping the track, the computer will resume the count when it is fixed.

In another corner of the building, transformers are assembled. A machine winds the laminations around a core, 12 cores at a time, and then they are varnished to protect against shorting. They are placed on a multi-shelved rolling tray and pushed into a big drying machine, named a "VB Vapor Blast," a name that sounds like a Star Wars toy.

Along the far wall of Plant 1, near the transformer section, are the track-making machines. They sit next to large reels of tinplate steel in bands that are 15/16-inch wide for 027 gauge and 1-3/16-inch wide for O gauge. The reels are fed into a forming machine, which bends the tinplate into the shape of a rail and then cuts it into strands. Some of the strands are kept straight and some are shaped into the various sized curves: 027, O and 072.

The strands travel to the end of the forming machine, where a device called a vibrator hopper pops a pin in the end of each rail. The strands are placed in boxes and taken to one of three different machines that make three-rail sections from individual rails. At one machine, used for 027 gauge, six workers attach the strands by hand to track clips. Then the sections travel through an automatic stamping machine where the rails and clips are pressed permanently together. The 027 gauge track is put together at this automatic machine because it is the fastest of the three and far more 027 gauge track is made than any of the others.

The slowest of the machines for making the sections is a hand-press machine, where the rails are joined to the fastener clips by hand. This is used on 072 and 054 gauge track be-

Area where transformer laminations are wound.

Tinplate bands which will be formed into track.

Track is shaped into curves.

O gauge track assembly machine from Hillside.

cause these are the lowest production items. The O gauge track is put together at an old, bulky machine at which workers sit in a circular assembly line. This process is slower than the 027 assembly method but faster than the hand press. The machine came from the old Lionel factory in New Jersey and is a nostalgic reminder of the days when Joshua Cowen might have been seen strolling through the factory, greeting workers by name.

Next to a huge storage area for MPC kits is an aisle where the old tooling from New Jersey is stored. The dies are packed in wooden crates with large numbers on them. The numbers conform to those on a master sheet kept in the engineering department.

On the other side of the MPC storage area is the customer service area, with many rows of bins filled with replacement parts, and a small repair room, where the actual servicing is done. This is next to what is called the "Finished Warehouse," where the boxed Lionel goods are stored awaiting shipment.

Plant No. 2 is dominated by 32 injection molding machines. These machines, not all of which are used for Lionel products, vary in size from 75 tons to 600 tons. Colored plastic, either in the form of a liquid or tiny pellets, is fed into the top of the machines. The rate that a molding machine produces an item will vary according to the item. Tenders will be produced at the rate of 70 an hour. A worker stands near a door of the molding machine and takes the item out as it is ready, trims it of the extra plastic and places it in a box. For items with high production runs, such as a coupler, of which 2½ million a year are made, the item is removed by a robot arm and swung over to a place where the extra plastic is cut off. The robot drops the excess into one bin and the coupler into another. The extra plastic is recycled. Most of the Lionel rolling stock is considered low production — 10,000 Mobil Gas tankers, which they were running in the spring of 1979, are nothing compared to 3 or 4 million plastic parts for an MPC kit — and robots are not used.

In 1979 Lionel was in the process of converting to liquid plastic from the old pellet system. Liquid is cheaper, takes less space to

Tooling storage area.

Bins of replacement parts.

Injection molding machines, liquid plastic on top.

Excess shot trimmed off tender after coming out of machine.

20

store, and Lionel engineers say it is easier to mix. When two different colors of pellets were mixed together to get a third color, it often happened that the color varied from batch to batch.

"I used to approve all the colors for Lionel," says Bill Diss, the head of administrative services. "You could get a red engine like the Katy switcher that had three different colors during its production run. You started creating collectors items. We don't want to do that."

After an item is molded it is sent to be painted. The paint room is located in another section of the building, away from the molding department. There are four different painting operations employed in the paint room:

1. — Solid, where the car is hand-sprayed one color.

2. — Mask — A mask, made of metal, covers the entire car except that area to be painted. Masks can be extremely expensive. The ones for the Santa Fe F-3s, with four different colors to apply, cost $9,000. One of the most elaborate masks Lionel made, although not the most expensive, was the one used on the vista dome of the aluminum cars.

3. — Springboard — On this an item is placed over a narrow opening and the paint is sprayed up. It is used to paint fairly flat surfaces like roofs or to paint stripes on a boxcar.

4 — Automatic — The items to be painted are placed on standards and pass, like ducks at a shooting gallery, through a U-shaped tunnel where they are painted and dried.

Once an item is painted, it is sent to the decorating department for the final application of graphics. Three different processes are used there: tampa, hot stamp, and electrocal. There are six tampa machines and 16 heat-stamping electrocal machines.

Tampa is a paint-like substance of a consistency somewhere between paint and ink, much like rubber-stamping. Tampa is applied directly onto the car and is used to paint irregular surfaces, like the stripes on the front of the 8854 CP Rail GP-9. Tampa machines can apply only one color at a time. The tampa application, which is heat-free, does not distort the plastic surface it is applied to. The heat process does distort, sometimes erasing rivets, for instance, on the sides of boxcars.

A hot-stamp machine has lettering that is engraved on a metal die. This is heated, then

Samples of colors and graphics awaiting approval.

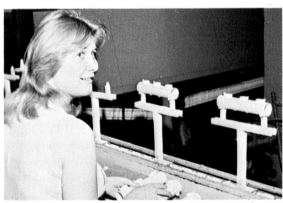

CP Rail boxcar sitting on mask before and after red triangle is applied.

Mobil gas tanker entering automatic paint machine.

Inside automatic painter.

pressed against a colored tape and it is the tape that is actually affixed to the car. Like tampa, hot-stamps can do only one color at a time.

Electrocal uses the same machines as the hot-stamps but without the dies. Electrocal is a decal that is transferred by heat onto the item. The decal is designed by Lionel, sent to a vendor to be made and placed on a roll of tape, hundreds to a roll, and then returned. Electrocals are used when multi-colors are needed, but they are applied most effectively on flat surfaces. When multi-colors are needed on surfaces that are not flat, such as the sides of tankers or the front of locos, regular pressure-sensitive decals are used. These are applied by hand on the final assembly line. Lionel uses a new type of decal that after 24 hours dries so hard that it is almost impossible to remove. It may be removed, however, immediately after it is first applied, so that if it goes on crooked it can be re-applied correctly. Until 1977 Lionel used the water slide-off type of decal and two workers would stand at the end of the assembly line with trays of water, applying the decals just like kids at home. Eventually, it appears certain, the electrocal process will become sophisticated enough to be applied to curved surfaces and hand-application of decals will be discontinued.

Along a wall next to the tampa and electrocal machines is a table with three rows of slats where examples of all of Lionel's graphics are kept. After the decals are returned from the vendor, they are checked against a corresponding example by someone from the art or engineering departments. Approval is required before the graphic can be applied to the production run. This section also contains heavy metal forms in the shape of the various cars and cabs Lionel makes. These forms are placed on the tampa and heat-stamping machines and the appropriate shell put over them when it is being decorated, thus assuring the same alignment every time.

There are three assembly lines in Plant 2 and all rolling stock is assembled there, as well as the cabs for diesels. Diesel cabs are sent back to Plant 1 for final assembly. When an item that is for separate sale is finished, whether in Plant 1 or Plant 2, it is boxed for shipment. If it is to be part of a set it is temporarily boxed and then re-boxed for shipment at Plant 1 when all the other items in the set get together in the final packing area.

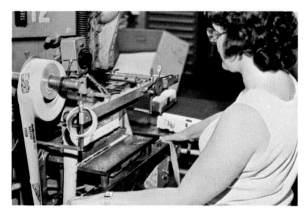

Applying electrocal to Good 'N Plenty car.

Tampa being applied to LCCA tanker.

Heat-stamping Burlington gondola.

Assembly of Sound-of-Steam tender.

Parts display board in Plant 1.

Final testing of a steamer.

Color samples on wall.

One last paint touch-up.

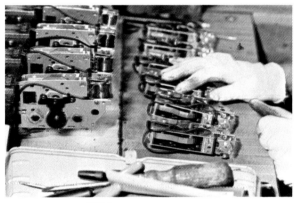
Wiring steamer motors.

Southern Pacific U36C awaiting final packaging.

Assembling steamer motors.

Packaged sets moving off assembly line.

Feeding tinplate into track-forming machine.

Workers placing clips on loose strands of track.

Track-forming machine.

Track about to have clips permanently affixed.

027 rails after being cut into straight sections.

Hand-pressing clips on 072 track.

Track strands after receiving pins.

After boxcars are molded they are placed on forms to
cool and prevent shrinking.

CP Rail boxcar before red triangle applied.

Heat-stamping Wabash gondola.

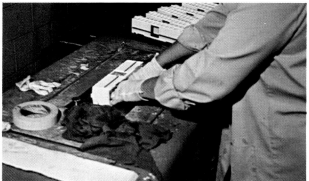

Springboard painting of stripe on LCCA boxcar.

Rear view of tampa machine.

Forms on which bodies are placed
before graphics are applied.

Customer repair shop in Plant 1.

Heat-stamping letters on LCCA car.

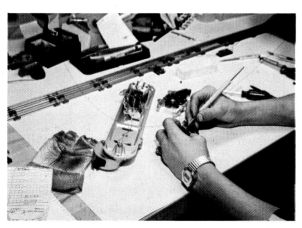

Repairs being made on an F-3.

25

PROTOTYPE: Southern Pacific Daylight

PROTOTYPE: Kansas City Southern F-3

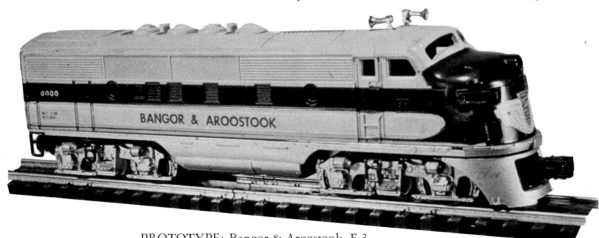

PROTOTYPE: Bangor & Aroostook, F-3

ARCHIVES

It was not until the early 1930s that the Lionel Corporation began to collect samples of its work. At first there seemed to be no grand strategy involved in the collection. There just happened to be a couple of empty showcases in the company's showrooms at 15 E. 26th Street in New York City.

"So I started putting old locomotives and cars in them," says Frank Pettit, who at that time was in charge of service repairs in the rear of the showrooms. "Customers would bring in old stuff and they'd be allowed 10 percent off the new list price. We were taking in so much old stuff we couldn't keep it all, even with the showcases, so a lot of it got thrown out. Who knew then what it would be worth?"

The overflowing showcases led to the establishment of the Lionel museum, where many rare old pieces were shown. In the meantime, the engineering department was keeping samples of its things: prototypes, mock-ups and production run items that had their engineering history attached to them. Many of the engineering samples and some of the museum things made their way to the second floor of the Hillside plant in the mid-1960s. That was during the era when Lionel was winding down its train operations. The museum was disbanded, the showrooms closed. The place on the second floor of the Hillside plant, a room with three-feet thick walls next to the engineering department, became known as the archives.

The archives were moved to Mount Clemens in 1970 and by that time they had become disorganized and decimated and they would continue to be in Michigan. In fact, for the 10-year period, 1966-1976, much of what was in the archives was stolen, lost, given away or broken.

"We have pictures of lots of Standard gauge items that were stolen," says Bill Diss, who is now in charge of the archives and who is finally making sure they are protected the way they should be.

There is much that is missing from the archives, but there is still much that is there. It is both interesting and useful. Diss examines the archives when considering new items to make. In 1979, when Lionel was planning its television commercial campaign, which had the theme of fathers passing on to sons the tradition of Lionel trains through the generations, Diss went to the archives and selected items from the 1920s, '30s, '40s, and '50s to be used in the films. It took him two weeks to get everything together. Some of the accessories were brand new out of the box.

The archives are still in a state of disarray, as the photographs show, but the long job of catagorizing them has begun. Eventually they will be organized and much of what is there displayed in a showroom. "We will have a showroom someday, somewhere," says Fundimensions president Jim Boosales. "The problem is picking a suitable spot. Mount Clemens is out of the way. Where should the stuff be displayed? New York or Chicago or perhaps the TCA museum? We have to figure all of that out."

The archives now are housed in a narrow, 80-foot-long room above the washrooms in Plant 1 in Mount Clemens. To get there one walks up 14 wooden steps, over exposed sprinkler pipes and through a locked wire gate and rickety wooden door. There, in 9-foot high sections of metal shelves and in boxes scattered and piled on the floor and in cabinets on the other side of the room, sits a fascinating array of Lionel productivity. The following pages show part of it.

PROTOTYPE: Frisco F-3

PROTOTYPE: Texas & Pacific F-3

PROTOTYPE: Atlanta & St. Andrews Bay F-3

PROTOTYPE: Bessemer F-3

PROTOTYPE: Missouri Pacific Lines F-3

PROTOTYPE: Southern Pacific F-3

PROTOTYPE: Union Pacific F-3

PROTOTYPE: Alaska Railroad F-3

PROTOTYPE: Florida East Coast F-3

PROTOTYPE: Atlantic Coast Line F-3

PROTOTYPE: Minneapolis & St. Louis F-3

PROTOTYPE: Western Maryland GP-9

PROTOTYPE: Chicago & North Western GP-7

PROTOTYPE: Grand Trunk Western GP-9

PROTOTYPE: DT&I GP-7

PROTOTYPE: Spokane Portland & Seattle Alco

PROTOTYPE: Hiawatha

MOCK-UP: Four-wheel dump car

100 B&O 1903-1905. Stolen.

First GG-1 made in Mount Clemens.

PROTOTYPE: Cab-forward steamer

PROTOTYPE: Candy car

No. 8 Trolley, 1911. Stolen.

30

PROTOTYPE: Missile launching
motorized unit

No. 42 Square cab with thick rims, repainted black.
Double motor. Made for the Lionel Museum. Only
one known. Stolen.

MOCK-UP: Jumping Gorilla car

PROTOTYPE: Southern Pacific GP-7

PROTOTYPE: Whistle shed

31

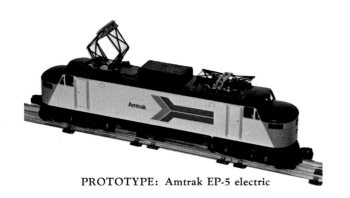

PROTOTYPE: Amtrak EP-5 electric

PROTOTYPE: Large-crane cab

773 boiler with marks indicating changes from prewar boiler.

MOCK-UP: Space car

PROTOTYPE: Lionel airplane

PROTOTYPE: Lionel transformer

PROTOTYPE: 6464-725 New Haven

MOCK-UP: Water refill accessory

PROTOTYPE: Baggage car

PROTOTYPE: New York Central Baldwin-type diesel

PROTOTYPE: Pennsylvania Baldwin-type diesel

PROTOTYPE: Gorilla & Keeper car

6057 Paint sample

PROTOTYPE: Lionel transformer

101 Summer Trolley. Factory repaint. Stolen.

MOCK-UP: Crate unloading car

PROTOTYPE: 3470 Target launcher

PROTOTYPE: Kansas City Southern Alco

MOCK-UP: Rifle and target toy

MOCK-UP: Target assembly

PROTOTYPE: Animal cage car, HO gauge

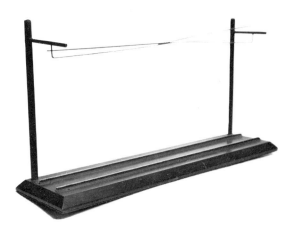

MOCK-UP: Cantenary system

PROTOTYPE: HO switcher

PROTOTYPE: Helicopter launching vehicle

PROTOTYPE: Space car

MOCK-UP: Central Control car

400 Trailer, 1901. Stolen.

200 Motorized, 1901. Stolen.

MOCK-UP: Hopper unloader without hopper.

Unloader with hopper

PROTOTYPE: 6445 Gold Reserve car

PROTOTYPE: Lionel Intercom

MOCK-UP: Changing billboard accessory

PROTOTYPE: Steamer with Hudson drivers

PROTOTYPE: Rocket Car

PROTOTYPE: Changing billboard accessory

Rocket car mechanism

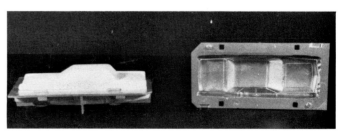

Plastic Lionel auto mold

PROTOTYPE: GB&W Alco

Lionel's stereo (3-D) camera.

MOCK-UP: Winch accessory

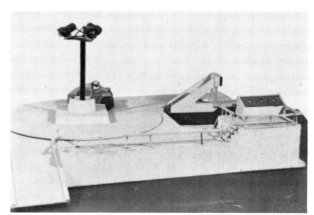

MOCK-UP: Unloader

1912 Special, numbered 54. Stolen.

3300 Summer Trolley. Motorized. Stolen.

MOCK-UP: Lift-truck accessory

PROTOTYPE: Space Center

PROTOTYPE: Candy car

PROTOTYPE: Postwar Lionel airplane

Operating car

PROTOTYPE: Molten steel dump car

MOCK-UP: Track gang accessory

PROTOTYPE: Animal cage car

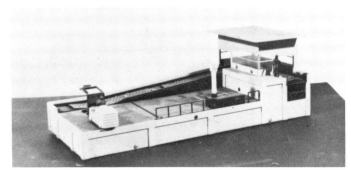

PROTOTYPE: Unloader

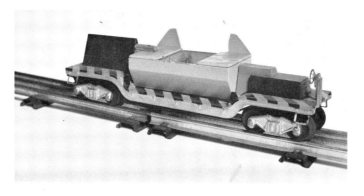

MOCK-UP: Depressed-center dump car

MOCK-UP: Wash rack

PROTOTYPE: 6413 Mercury project capsule car

PROTOTYPE: Motorized unit

PROTOTYPE: Helicopter launching station

PROTOTYPE: Oil storage unit

MOCK-UP: Operating giraffe car

PROTOTYPE: Burlington GP-7

MOCK-UP: Track Repair tender

MOCK-UP: Rail Attack tender

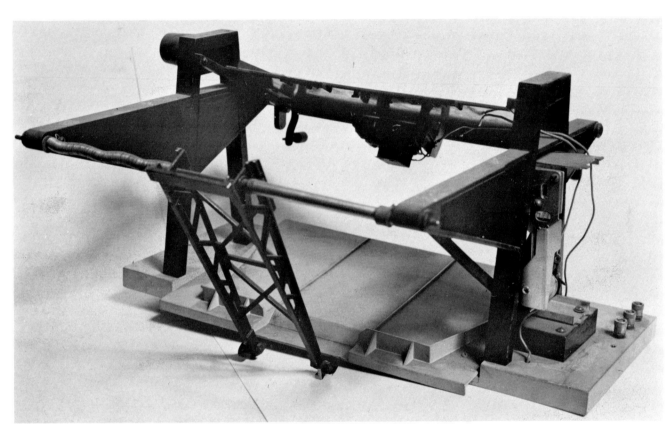

MOCK-UP: Unloading accessory

PROTOTYPE: Lumber mill and shed

PROTOTYPE: Lionel transformer

PROTOTYPE: Lionel transformer

MOCK-UP: Trackside building and signal

PROTOTYPE: Rocket launching car

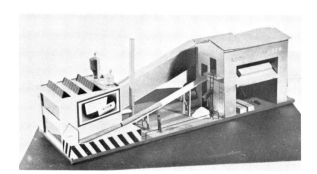

PROTOTYPE: Lumber mill and shed

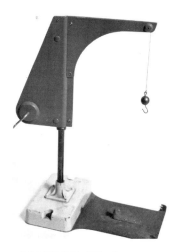

MOCK-UP: Winch accessory

No. 3 Trolley with open three-rivet trucks. Stolen.

Prototype: US Gypsum

300 Open Trolley, 1902-1904. Stolen.

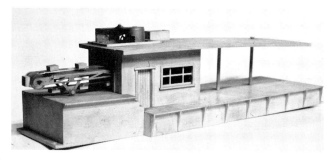

MOCK-UP: Operating conveyor belt accessory

GP-7s & GP-9s

1776 Norfolk & Western
8254 Illinois Central
8255 Santa Fe
8358 Pennsylvania
8561 Jersey Central

1776 (8665) Jeremiah O'Brien
8030 Illinois Central
8250 Santa Fe
8357 Pennsylvania
8550 Jersey Central

The Electro-Motive Division of General Motors brought out their first road switcher, the GP-7, in 1949 and it was an immediate success. A total of 74 different railroads bought it between 1949 and 1954, when the GP-9s came out. Even more railroads bought the GP-9.

The Lionel division of General Mills has been doing all right with their GP-7s and -9s, too. Between 1970 and 1980 Lionel offered them in 21 different road names, more than any other engine they made. The difference between Lionel's GP-7 and GP-9 is that the -7 has no dynamic brake blister and the GP-9 does. That is not the distinguishing characteristic on the real engines, however. Both the -7s and -9s came with or without dynamic brakes. The difference was that the -9s had more horsepower, 1,750, as opposed to the 7s' 1,500, and, externally, the -7s had more rows of louvres than the -9s (see *Lionel: A Collector's Guide, Vol. II* for a more detailed explanation of the real geeps).

The present Lionel model is not as good mechanically as the GP-7s and -9s made by the old company through 1966. Those had a better motor, die-cast power trucks and Magne-Traction. The present geeps have a stamped sheet metal power truck, although the truck sideframes themselves are still die-cast. There is no Magne-Traction today.

The present motor is the same size as the older one; it has the same size armature and magnetic field and has the same amperage draw, but instead of the motor and truck assembly being separate units, with power transmitted by internal spur gearing to geared axles, the new geeps have a motor and truck assembly that is one unit, with gears that are made of nylon. It does not run as well as the other motor and it does not pull as many cars.

The reason it does not pull as well is because it lacks Magne-Traction. In place of Magne-Traction the new geeps have a rubber tire around the drive wheels. The rubber tire is merely slipped over the wheel and when heated it expands and comes off easily. If the engine has a heavy load the rubber tires make it stutter, what operators call "wheel-hop", and it chatters on the track. The loose rubber tire can be secured better by using an adhesive, but most operators wish Lionel would resurrect Magne-Traction.

The reasons the new geep motor does not run well are several, including the new nylon gears. The nylon gears were placed on the new geeps because they were cheaper and quieter and, according to Lionel engineers, life-tests showed them to wear better than metal. But some repairmen complain that the nylon gears have stripped.

"The wheel-hop causes the worm gear to vibrate and that chews the heck out of the gears," says one. "The nylon gears on the spur side aren't too bad, but the main pinion gear always slips."

Besides motor problems, the geeps have had a history of wheel trouble and a resulting tendency to wobble. Three things contribute to the wobbling: first, the wheel with the rubber tire is not always the exact same size as the wheels on the opposite side; second, sometimes the wheels are not pressed on the axles correctly; and third, the new geeps have zinc wheels instead of sintered-iron and the zinc wheels have some uneven surfaces caused by a parting line left when they are taken out of the casting die.

The characteristics of the GP-7s and GP-9s so far discussed are also applicable to the GP-20s, U36Bs and Cs and SD-18s. They all use the same motor. The F-3s, F-Ms, electrics and Budd cars use the two-unit motor, the same motor, actually, that was in the old GP-7s and -9s. The two types of motors are the only drive systems Lionel used on its diesels and electrics through the 1970s.

The frame of the old Lionel GP-7s and GP-9s was altered somewhat to accommodate the new one-piece motor-truck assembly (which is much like the motor Lionel used on their switchers in 1955, when the drive system was downgraded). A large hole was punched into the bottom of the frame, along with new guide slots. The fuel tanks are also slightly shorter than on the original version.

The handrails on the frames of the geeps and U-boats changed throughout the years. First they were wire and attached to metal stanchions, but that only lasted one year.

The stanchions were changed to plastic in 1972. Finally, in 1975, the handrails and stanchions began to be stamped, as they had been on the original geeps of the 1950s.

Metal supports.   Plastic supports.   Stamped handrails.

The Lionel GP-7s and -9s did not undergo many year-by-year technical changes during the first decade of manufacture by General Mills. That is also true of all other items made by the new Lionel. The reason for this is that in the great majority of cases Lionel only makes one production run. That run, as best as can be estimated, has generally been in the area of 6,000 pieces for top-of-the-line locos. An item is cataloged a second year only if the original inventory is not sold out. Variations that do occur usually involve decoration mix-ups rather than changes in production methods. With old Lionel an item was kept in the line as long as it sold well. That could mean many years of cataloging it (18 for the old Santa Fe F-3), with repeated production runs that would offer the possibilities of variations in manufacturing methods.

But in spite of the evenness of the yearly production runs, some items are still more in demand with collectors than others. It is not because they are any rarer in many cases that their worth is driven up, but because they are more popular.

The interest in the overall Lionel product is still there among collectors, even if the technical aspects of it require less explanation. In this section and those that follow the authors will take a closer look, rather brief in some cases, at all the major items put out under the Lionel name in its first decade under General Mills.

8030 ILLINOIS CENTRAL & 8254 DUMMY

The 8030 GP-9 was cataloged in 1970, '71 and '72. The first year some of the bodies were molded from orange plastic and only the white was painted on. Later versions were molded of gray plastic and both the orange and white were painted.

The frames on the 1971 version had wire handrails which were supported by the same metal stakes Lionel used on their log car in the 1950s. Collectors complained that the stakes made the car look like a log car with a geep cab.

The third-rail pick-up assemblies caused trouble on the 1971 model. Newly developed in New Jersey, they had trouble going through switches because the rollers were hollow and too light. They also had a tendency to pick up dirt, causing shorts which would unexpectedly cause the engine to reverse directions.

Early hollow pick-ups.   Left-over Hillside pick-ups.   Snap-in roller pick-ups.

The pick-up assembly with its hollow rollers stayed on the 8030 in 1971 but in 1972 the unit was improved. The hollow rollers were replaced with solid, snap-in rollers attached to an axle. These were the same type used on passenger cars and cabooses and were an improvement over those they replaced, but they still cause trouble because they fall out a lot. The best type of pick-up assembly was the one used on the original Lionel geeps. Some 8030 Illinois Centrals and other early geeps had the good pick-up assembly but they were left-overs from Hillside.

A 8031 dummy unit was cataloged with the 8030 in 1970 but it was never made. The Illinois Central dummy did not come out until 1972 and it was given the number 8254. It had plastic stanchions for the wire handrails. Since many of the 8030 power units did not have the plastic stanchions it meant that the power units did not exactly match their dummies, the only time that happened except for the 8031 Canadian National and some of its 8258 dummies.

The number of the 8031 Illinois Central dummy that was never made was reassigned to the Canadian National power unit. Lionel uses the second digit of their catalog number to designate the year an engine was made, al-

8655 Boston & Maine
8668 Northern Pacific
8854 CP Rail
8760 Erie Lackawanna
8778 Lehigh Valley
8867 Minneapolis & St. Louis

though there are some exceptions to this system. Harry Blum, the first General Mills manager of operations in Hillside, started the 8000 numbering series back in 1969 when the 1970 line was still being planned. The year 1980 will mean that zero numbers will again be in demand, just as in 1981 "one" numbers will be, and so on every year through the decade; but Lionel engineering administrator Bill Diss says there are enough 8000-series numbers to make it through.

Most dealers report dummy sales lag behind powered units 2-to-1. They feel they would sell more dummies if they were illuminated. The word from Lionel is that after 1979 most geeps, U-boats and SD-18s will be illuminated. The price will go up.

8031 CANADIAN NATIONAL & 8258 DUMMY

Neither the Canadian National GP-7 power unit nor the dummy was cataloged in the United States but they did appear in the Canadian catalog issued by Lionel in 1971 (the power unit) and 1972 (the dummy). Some of the early engines have the metal handrail stanchions. Later ones have the plastic. The same is true of the pick-up assemblies; the early ones have the hollow rollers, the later ones the solid.

The dummy units have the plastic stanchion and when they appear with the metal-stanchioned power unit they join the Illinois Central as the only road names to have power units that don't match their dummies.

8250 SANTA FE GP-7 & 8255 DUMMY

1972 through 1974. Some collectors think Lionel made this black engine because there were Canadian National cabs left over. "The correct color is dark blue," says one, Patti Nicholson of Chicago. "I think they figured black was close enough and put yellow Santa Fe lettering on them."

8359 CHESSIE GP-7

1973. This was General Motors' 50th anniversary year and the Chessie System had an engine painted gold and marked "GM 50." Collector Leonard Tangent remembers seeing the engine at General Motors' Electro-Motive plant in La Grange, Illinois. "I was at an open house at the plant and they had an engine painted just like Lionel's, but it wasn't a GP-7. It was a GP-40."

8654 Boston & Maine
8666 Northern Pacific
8757 Conrail
8759 Erie Lackawanna
8775 Lehigh Valley
8866 Minneapolis & St. Louis

The Chessie System, which is quite co-operative with Lionel, sent the engineering department paint chips and photos, but there was opposition to the gold engine.

"I had quite a time convincing marketing that we should make that unit," says Dick Branstner, who was then vice-president of engineering for Lionel. "Everyone said it would be a flop and, of course, we all know that was not the case." There are reports that 9,000 were made on a limited run basis. "For quite a while after its success, marketing people would always ask, 'Hey, Branstner, don't you have another gold Chessie up your sleeve?' Of all the road names we made at Lionel, my favorite had to be the gold Chessie."

Some Chessies exist without the "GM 50" on the side. It was a factory omission but collectors value it more than the regular run version with the complete set of graphics.

8357 PENNSYLVANIA GP-9 & 8358 DUMMY

1973 and 1974. An engine with Pennsylvania markings is usually a good seller, for it is one of the railroads to which Lionel repeatedly returns. The state of Pennsylvania is the Mecca of train enthusiasts, both real and model. It is one of the largest toy train markets in the country and is where the biggest train meet, at York, is held every year.

8353 GRAND TRUNK GP-9 & 8356 DUMMY

1973 through 1975. The Grand Trunk is a local Detroit line and its tracks pass within sight of the Lionel administrative offices. Dick Branstner thought the Grand Trunk's paint scheme was a colorful one and was instrumental in working out the details with the railroad. They supplied Lionel with photos and graphics.

8454 RIO GRANDE GP-7 & 8455 DUMMY

1974 and 1975. The Rio Grande, which has become a popular engine, was the first to which Lionel applied stripes to the ends. Bill Diss only wanted to do the Rio Grande if they could find a way to apply the safety stripes. "Without the stripes," says Diss, "it is a very dull engine."

The methods Lionel was using to apply stripes in 1974 were not suitable for irregular surfaces. After a bit of experimentation, it was found the tampa process was suitable for the job. Tampa put the stripes on without obliterating the cab detail, something that can happen with the heat process (see FACTORY for further details on decorating). Some slight modifications on the GP-7 die were required to accommodate the tampa process.

"That's how we discover new decorating techniques," says Diss. "New schemes will show up that we want to do and we try to figure out how. Eventually we are able to do things that a few years earlier we would have never attempted."

8550 JERSEY CENTRAL GP-9 & 8561 DUMMY

1975 and 1976. The Jersey Central Railroad and Lionel seem to have a strange relationship. It is strange that Lionel would want to continue it. Back in 1956 Lionel came out with the famous Fairbanks-Morse Trainmaster in the Jersey Central colors. It is famous now because it was such a poor seller that it became one of the rarest of the postwar pieces. For some reason, however, the new Lionel people decided they would try the Jersey Central again, this time on a GP-9. The Jersey Central Railroad was not cooperative. They gave the engineering department little help with their new color scheme. But Lionel decided to go ahead anyway.

They really didn't need much help in figuring out the graphics. They are so simple and unimaginative they were easy to do, which was one of the considerations in selecting the road name. Lionel did not sell out the production run in 1975. It was cataloged again in 1976 and finally sold out. Says an eastern collector: "I can never figure that railroad out. They change paint schemes with the seasons. They went from dark green with yellow lettering to blue with orange and now red with white. They must change every time they get a good buy on paint. Lionel's version is an accurate reproduction of the original. It's ugly but accurate."

8576 PENN CENTRAL GP-9

1976 and 1977. The people in the engineering department at Lionel say this engine was marketing's idea. The people in engineering usually say that when a dull-colored engine appears on the market, an item that is pretty much guaranteed to mean sluggish sales. The people in marketing don't remember whose idea it was.

The most significant thing about the 8576 Penn Central was that it was the first geep with stamped metal handrails. The U36B Spirit of 1776, which came out in 1975, was the first engine to have the handrails. On these first engines the rails were riveted to the frame; on newer engines the rails are spot-welded on.

Lionel had received complaints about the wire handrails and since the stamped rails were cheaper to make, the switch was made. Some paint combinations were being planned that would call for painted handrails and that was another reason for converting to the stamped rails. But between 1976 and 1979 one end of the stamped handrails was secured to the cab near the window. When the cab was removed for repairs the rails would scrape against it and and leave scratches. After receiving many complaints Lionel straightened the railings so they were no longer attached to the cabs.

"There was grief right from the beginning with the rails that secured to the cabs," says Bill Diss. "Cabs were scratched during assembly at the factory." The reason Lionel did not change the stamping immediately was because they wanted to use the inventory of the curved stampings before they started making the straight railings.

8665 JEREMIAH O'BRIEN GP-9

1976. All the railroads had fancy Bicentennial color schemes on at least one engine or train. Some were more elaborate than others. Some would have been beyond Lionel's capacity to reproduce in a feasibly-priced model. The top choice of the Lionel executives at first seemed to be the Milwaukee Road's engine, which had an unfurled American flag, rippling in the wind, painted along its entire side. The production department laughed when asked about the possibility of doing that engine.

The second favorite of the engineering department seemed to be a Bangor and Aroostook GP-7, which was named after a Maine patriot who, in 1775, led a group of civilians in an attack against an armed British warship and captured it after killing its commanding officer. The color scheme of the Bangor and Aroostook's engine was not only attractive, it was within Lionel's decorating capabilities.

A matching caboose was included. The two items were good for people who wanted a Bicentennial commemorative piece but who did not want to buy an entire set, such as the State set, which had a U36B heading a 13-boxcar consist, each car representing one of the original colonies.

The Jeremiah O'Brien had a circle of stars on the cab beneath the window, but on some engines the stars were accidently not put on.

8559-1776 NORFOLK & WESTERN GP-9

1976. The number 8559 does not appear on the engine, but it does appear on the box. The only number on this Bicentennial special was 1776.

Bill Diss, who in recent years has had the greatest single influence at Lionel over what road names are picked for the line, first saw a photograph of the Norfolk & Western prototype in a magazine named *Extra 2200 South,* a monthly that features stories and pictures of new diesels. "I thought it was better looking than the Seaboard Coastline job so I brought it up to the marketing and production people and we decided to do it," Diss says. "We had problems with the circle of stars. I'm sure collectors are aware of the variations. We first used hot stamping but later tried to improve the looks and switched methods. You can see the results. Those made during the last run have much crisper markings."

Changing methods for applying graphics is one of the principal ways variations can occur at Lionel. Another common way is for someone to merely forget to add a decoration, such as the ring of stars on the Jeremiah O'Brien. Colors sometimes vary, too. Lionel has recently switched to using liquid plastic instead of plastic pellets in the molding machines. The pellets used to result in inconsistencies of colors from batch to batch on the same item, thus creating variations.

The Norfolk & Western came in a five-car set with a matching caboose.

8654 BOSTON & MAINE GP-9 & 8655 DUMMY

1976. An old Lionel favorite, the 8654 was the first new Lionel engine to have the frame and handrails painted. John Brady, former assistant products manager at Lionel, says the main reason the company switched to stamped handrails was "because we wanted to paint them. And, of course, they were easier for us during assembly."

8666 NORTHERN PACIFIC GP-9 & 8668 DUMMY

1976. The 8666 headed the service station set in 1976. It came with a green and silver caboose, as it did on the real railroad. But collectors complained that the caboose should match the engine, so Lionel made a matching caboose that had no real prototype. There were less complaints about the caboose that was wrong than the one that was right.

"We like to stay as close to the real world as possible," says marketing manager Pete Sappenfield, "but you can't always do that."

The dummy unit was available in 1976 but did not come with the set.

8750 THE ROCK GP-7 & 8751 DUMMY

1977 and 1978. This is another color combination that came about because of the magazine *Extra 2200 South.* The magazine likes to show pictures of color combinations when they are still in experimental stages. Most railroads experiment by painting one engine or boxcar to see how it looks. If it is not satisfactory, changes are made before the final choices are made. The Lionel engineering and marketing departments conferred about using the Rock graphics almost as soon as the magazine came out. Both agreed it was a comtemporary and colorful look and production scheduling was begun immediately.

Conrail geep at Niles, Michigan, depot.

8757 CONRAIL GP-9

1977 and 1978. The consensus seems to be that the blue on the 8757 is too dark. Lionel admits the possibility.

"The blue may be off but it matches perfectly the color sample Conrail sent us," says Bill Diss. "But they sent it before they made any large quantity of engines so maybe they decided to change the shade after they sent us the chip."

Paint chips come to Lionel from the railroads in many different sizes and on a variety of materials. Sometimes Lionel receives a one-inch square of the color, sometimes a full-size perforated sheet with adhesive backs so the color can be stuck on the piece to see how it matches. Sometimes metal is sent, sometimes plastic.

"They never go out and actually chip a piece of paint off a loco," says Diss.

In Conrail's case, Lionel was sent a complete logo and color package through the Conrail advertising agency. It explained where the logo should be placed and included tear sheets of the color. "They were very particular how their logo was used and about getting their color right," says Diss. "It was like working with a bunch of lawyers. We matched the color they sent us, but as I said, they might have changed their minds later."

Lionel has found that Conrail is a great experimenter, and so is Amtrak. Amtrak first tried painting red and blue lines all the way around their engines before settling on the arrow motif and Conrail at one point tried red oxide and white boxcars and engines. They made one of each. Lionel saw an early photograph of the red boxcar and rushed one into production. Lionel was later criticized for making a red boxcar, since hardly anyone had seen the original red experimental model — which never went into full production — but the fact is Conrail did have one.

8759 ERIE-LACKAWANNA GP-9 & 8760 DUMMY

1977 through 1979. The idea for the 8759 arose from an ad in a train magazine. The ad was selling color slides of different diesels. The Erie-Lackawanna stood out because it was so colorful. Besides it was from a prime marketing area.

The 8759 proved to be a very difficult item to paint. No photos or information were sent to Lionel from the Erie-Lackawanna because at the time they were in the process of being absorbed by Conrail. Working from the color slides and other sources, the Lionel team was able to get a nice model of an engine with a three-color body and yellow painted frame, the most intricate scheme they had yet undertaken.

"We used a combination of paint masks and heat-stamps to pull it off," says Diss. "I was very happy with the results."

8763 NORFOLK & WESTERN GP-9

1977 and 1978. Lionel's marketing department has always had strong feelings about the Norfolk & Western name. This is the main explanation for their rush to get out an engine of such bland graphics, an eagerness that has perplexed many collectors.

In 1977 the Norfolk & Western had just come out with their new logo and marketing wanted to exploit it immediately. They did, but the collectors were not very impressed.

"Maybe they had a bunch of Penn Central black bodies left over," was a typical comment. There might be a little truth in that: certainly marketing was aware that the one-color graphic would be cheap to produce.

"Some collectors think we should charge less when it's a one-color scheme," says products man John Brady. "But we don't charge more when we do three colors."

Southern dummy units ready for shipping.

8774 SOUTHERN GP-9 & 8758 DUMMY

1977. Another attractive color scheme, although technically it is not the correct current colors of the Southern Railroad. Back in the 1950s they painted their road diesels green and white — but with yellow lettering, not gold. The white is wrong, too. It should be more an ivory tone rather than snow white.

The Southern has always been extremely co-operative with Lionel. Its former president, W. Graham Claytor, acting secretary of transportation in the Carter Administration, is a model railroad buff and charter member of the Train Collectors Association.

8775 LEHIGH VALLEY GP-9
& 8778 DUMMY

1977 and 1978. The Lehigh Valley was the most ambitious color combination Lionel had attempted to that time. It is the first time Lionel did a logo within the safety stripes on the front. The engine was first painted white then, using the tampa process, the black stripes were added, along with the logo.

"We wanted to do the Erie-Lackawanna, Lehigh Valley and some others before they were absorbed by Conrail and their identity lost to the public," says Diss. We had a difficult time choosing the Lehigh Valley because they have so many variations. They have all white locos with dark lettering, all red with white lettering. We chose this one because we thought it was the best, not necessarily the latest."

The color of the red, however, is slightly off. It is a bright red and should be a cordovan.

8854 CP RAIL GP-9

1978 and 1979. Originally Lionel had planned to make a CP Rail GP-20 in 1974, but it was stopped in production after a prototype, now in the archives, was made up. The 8854 is a fine model, but once again the red is a little off. It should be an orangy red rather than a bright red.

RATING

1. 8666 Northern Pacific and 8668 NP Dummy
2. 8359 Chessie Gold
3. 1776 Norfolk and Western (8559 on box)
4. 8665 Jeremiah O'Brien

Photos courtesy of Philip and Carolyn Sayer

Lionel showroom layout, August, 1956.

GP-20s

The GP-20 was the first time the new Lionel broke the mold, so to speak. Until the 8352 Santa Fe GP-20 was introduced in 1973, Mount Clements had made only diesels that had been made by the old Lionel. For the GP-20, engineering vice-president Dick Branstner decided to retool. The veep liked the geep.

It was a simple job. Branstner went to his tool and die expert, Fred Binder, and told him he wanted to make a low-nosed unit using the high-nosed GP-7 tool. Binder looked it over. He decided to make an insert for the tool that would cut the side of the nose in half. When the insert was attached, the tool would make GP-20s; when it was removed, it would again make GP-7s.

Lionel picked the 8355 dummy as the first recipient of its newly developed electronic horn. It turned out to be not quite developed enough. The horn sounded good but there were faulty contacts in the controller system. The control unit was actually a rectifier, converting AC power to DC when a button on the transformer was pushed. As DC was introduced, the horn sounded. It made a fine sound; the horn itself worked well. The problem was that the contacts would not disengage when the button was released. The unit would overheat and eventually burn up.

There were two GP-20 dummy units that came with the electronic horn: the 8355 Santa Fe and the 8367 Long Island. Lionel, after outfitting these two dummies with the horn, had about 1,200 left over. Those they put in the 8573 Union Pacific U36B dummy. These Union Pacific dummies are extremely hard to find now.

8352 SANTA FE & 8355 DUMMY

1973 through 1975. On the surface, the GP-20 seemed like a good idea. But the GP-20s never achieved much popularity with collectors and it took three years for Lionel to get rid of all its Santa Fe's. Perhaps the introduction the next year of the U36B, the first low-nose diesel Lionel made from completely new dies, detracted from the appeal of the hybrid GP-20s. In any case, neither the Santa Fe nor any other GP-20, except the Chessie, created much excitement.

8360 LONG ISLAND & 8367 DUMMY

1973. The 8360 Long Island was shown in the catalog with an orange stripe along the frame. The 1973 advance catalog showed it with a dark roof and light body. It was not made either of those ways, but it probably should have been. The production piece was drab and there was not exactly a public clamor over it.

8463 CHESSIE

1974. This was the one GP-20 that was popular. It reflects, no doubt, the handsome graphics that the Baltimore & Ohio adopted at that time. The B&O is very good about keeping Lionel informed on any new Chessie paint scheme. As soon as the catchy cat-inside-the-C design was approved by the railroad, it sent photographs and paint chips to Lionel, which began preparations immediately to make Chessie items.

8562 MISSOURI PACIFIC & 8565 DUMMY

1975 and 1976. A very handsome model, the graphics of which look exactly like its prototype, it nevertheless took two years to sell out. Some were made without the MoPac decal on the side of the door. It was the last GP-20 to come with the wire handrails. The 8565 dummy was the first GP-20 dummy without the electronic horn.

8772 GULF MOBILE & OHIO

1977. It was the first GP-20 to come with a painted frame and the first to have stamped handrails. It is one of the harder GP-20s to find because it came only in a set and fewer sets are made than engines for separate sale, which all of the other GP-20s were.

8776 CHICAGO & NORTH WESTERN & 8779 DUMMY

1977. The colorful North Western color scheme was chosen because the Chicago area is one of Lionel's biggest markets. In 1980 Lionel would go to the C&NW scheme again with an FM and matching bay window caboose.

RATING

1. Chessie
2. GM&O

8355 Santa Fe
8367 Long Island
8772 Gulf Mobile & Ohio
8565 Missouri Pacific
8779 Chicago & Northwestern

8352 Santa Fe
8360 Long Island
8463 Chessie
8562 Missouri Pacific
8776 Chicago & Northwestern

F-3s

During its first decade under General Mills, Lionel made F-3s in 10 different road names and six of them had been among the rarest of the old F-3s. The policy was to bring back the collector items.

Lenny Dean

The moving force behind this decision was Lenny Dean, the widely admired service manager who has been associated with Lionel for more than 30 years. Dean felt strongly from the beginning of the new era that the old favorite of the collectors should be reissued. Dean is one of the old employees from New Jersey who stayed with the company and in New Jersey after the takeover by General Mills. He managed the parts department there until it was finally moved to Mount Clemens in 1979. He is now a consultant. His main advice now, as it has been since Dick Branstner began exploring a possible new line in 1969: emphasize quality.

But as Lionel moves into the second decade of its new era, indications are that they are going to start reaching beyond the old names and begin issuing color combinations never before offered. There are many nice road names to pick from. A look at the F-3s that are in the archives alone would provide several years worth of interesting models (see AR-CHIVES). And in all deference to the venerable Lenny Dean, not all collectors wanted so many of the old items reissued in the first place.

Those collectors who had the original pieces wanted to see new road names. New collectors who didn't want to spend the money required to establish a collection of originals were happy to see remakes of the classics. There is also the question of value. Most collectors feel that a reissue causes the value of the original to go down, but that is not a certainty. What is certain is that the *market* for the original goes down upon a reissuance, but the price does not necessarily have to go down. There will always be purists who will want the original. To the seller a reissuance may mean he will have to hold on to his piece a little longer, but he should eventually get his price. In the long run, everyone should benefit. The trains being made today are attracting new collectors, some of whom will eventually be in the market for the originals. If it weren't for the new trains, they might never have become collectors at all.

The new F-3 is essentially the same as the single-motored model of the '50s. The new units have no horn or Magne-Traction, but they have the same motor and power truck, except that on the power truck the idler gear and pinion gear are nylon rather than brass. But the worm gear is brass, just like the old one.

The frame is still made of cast-metal, but it has reenforcing brackets inside the belly tanks. There is an operating coupler on the front and a fixed coupler on the rear, as there were on the original model. The numberboards are clear plastic and do not have the number of the engine stamped on them. The old ones did.

The first F-3s made in 1973 had decorative horns on the roof, but they were made of "metalized" plastic. These horns broke easily and therefore, in 1976, starting with the Santa Fe, they were changed to die-cast, like the old horns. In 1978 a twin-motored unit was made and in 1979 the Pennsylvania had clear plastic portholes and grab-irons on the front of the cab below the windows. That meant that the most detailed F-3 made in Mount Clemens, the 8952 Pennsylvania, had almost as much detail as the most detailed of the models in the '50s, lacking only numbers on the number boards, wire mesh under the roof louvres, and ladders under the front door. But it should be remembered that by the end of the '50s much of that good detail was gone from the old engines, too, so that the present day F-3 is better in many ways than most of the old F-3s. It also costs more.

There are some external variations having to do with the number of louvres between the portholes. These can vary anywhere from one to four, depending on the graphics that will appear on the side. The louvres can be taken out by inserting plugs in the die. The decision to leave them in or take them out is based on how much flat surface is needed for decoration. The 8464 Rio Grande, for instance, has all four louvres in place, while the 8466 Amtrak has three louvres removed for the arrow design on the side. If you look closely at the Amtrak unit you can see a little square where the plug covered the louvres in the die.

8363 BALTIMORE & OHIO A
8364 DUMMY — 8468 B UNIT

1973 through 1975. The old Baltimore & Ohio was one of the two most sought after F-3s made by the old Lionel. The new Lionel selected it to be its first F-3. The 8363 was painted a flat white and blue, as opposed to the originals, which were unpainted blue plastic.

The flat white gets dirty easily and some collectors wax it to keep it clean and make it look better. The striping on the side of the cab is applied by the electrocal process, which could not be applied to the nose (see page 22). The striping on the nose was applied by decal. As a consequence, at the point where the decal

Dan Johns

stripe met the electrocaled stripe — under the numberboard — the stripes did not line up correctly. But the engineers at Lionel learned from the experience. After that, on engines like the Milwaukee Road, they ran the decal stripe all the way to the front door, then resumed the stripe with electrocal on the other side of the door.

The dummy units came out the same year as the powered units but the 8468 B unit did not come out until 1974, Lionel thus establishing a policy of coming out with B units a year after the A. The B units were distributed only through service stations and they arrived unassembled. Dan Johns, who now heads Lionel's customer service department, explained the B unit policy: "We would sell the A units all the way through our sales network. If the A units were accepted, then we came out with a B unit. If not, we wouldn't. We would make about 80 per cent as many B units as we sold A units. The reason we distributed only through service stations was we wanted to give them some exclusive business. It cost a little less to have the B units assembled by the dealers."

A problem arose because the A units and B units were made at different times. They used different masks and as a result the gray on the roof of the B&O A unit comes down farther than it does on the B unit. The problem was discovered during the production run of the B units and it was corrected, but that has created a variation. Some 8468 B units match the 8363 A units and some do not.

8365 CANADIAN PACIFIC A
8366 DUMMY — 8369 B UNIT

1973. B Unit 1974. The original Canadian Pacific of the 1950s became the most valuable of Lionel's F-3s. The 8365 has become the most valuable of the F-3s of the 1970s. It headed an uncataloged service station set and that, too, has become the most prized of all the service station sets.

The B units which came out in 1974 did not all match the A units. The striping, as in the case with the B&O B units, was sometimes off. The reason was the same: different mask jobs that were corrected during production.

There is another variation on the Canadian Pacific B units. On most the number 8469 is on the far left side and the lettering is off center to the right. A few were made, however, with the lettering on the far right side and the number off center to the left.

8466 AMTRAK A
8467 DUMMY — 8475 B UNIT

1974 and 1975. B unit 1975. This was the first new road name assigned to new Lionel F-3s. Two sets of louvres were removed from the right of the first porthole to accommodate the Amtrak arrow.

The Amtrak B unit came out in 1975. Unlike the first two B units, it came assembled and boxed. The problems with the masking remained, though. It did not match the A unit.

The Amtrak engine became immediately popular because Williams Electric Trains put out a set of aluminum cars with Amtrak markings. By matching the Williams cars and the Lionel engine, one could have a complete Amtrak set.

8555 MILWAUKEE ROAD A
8557 DUMMY — 8575 B UNIT

1975. B Unit 1976. The most notable thing about the ABA Milwaukee Road is that the B unit finally matched the A units. They were both painted a solid gray. The old Lionel version of the Milwaukee Road F-3 was painted a glossy gray, but this version is dull. "We had a lot of flat paint to get rid of in those days," says Bill Diss. The B unit was, however, glossy.

Boxed Milwaukee Road F-3s.

Diss, incidentally, was against the reissuance of this engine. He felt the color scheme was

too drab. "The Milwaukee Road has a lot of different color combinations and graphics to choose from. I thought it was unfortunate to choose this one."

8464 RIO GRANDE
8465 DUMMY
8474 B UNIT

1974. B unit 1975. This engine headed an uncataloged service station set. It's a remake of an item from the '50s and it is reported that only 3,000 were made, but it is not particularly popular among collectors. Certainly when compared with the old 2379 Rio Grande, the 8464 comes off badly. The trouble is the paint.

The engine should be predominantly orange, but Lionel made it yellow. The nose color of the real Rio Grande F-3 is a subdued olive, not bright green. Once again, flat paint was used by Lionel and that did not help matters.

The Rio Grande did send paint chips to Lionel, but somehow the colors did not end up matching. That could be due to the fact that sometimes Lionel will use a paint they have in stock, if it is close enough to the color chip, instead of mixing a new batch to match the chip exactly. The paint chip Lionel received for the Rio Grande nose was very close to Lionel's Penn Central green and they used it on the Rio Grande. It turned out that this did not come close to matching the green on the protoype, but then railroads sometimes do not match their own paint chips when it comes time to paint the engine.

Rio Grande F-unit.

Lionel's 8474 B unit came out the next year and, however inaccurate the colors might have been, they matched those of the A unit.

Until the Rio Grande, all the F-3s had been made in New Jersey. The Rio Grande was the first F-3 to be made entirely in Mount Clemens, although the cabs had always been molded there.

8568 PREAMBLE EXPRESS

1975. In 1974 Lionel made plans to produce a Freedom Train, modeled after the real Freedom Train that was going to tour the United States the next year with artifacts from American history. There was also going to be a diesel-powered Preamble Express that was to tour the United States in advance of the Freedom Train, check out the track, and make arrangements for the arrival of the big train. Lionel's Diss planned a Preamble Express, too, as a companion to the Freedom Train. The Freedom train, consisting of old-style passenger cars Lionel had brought out in 1973, would be pulled by a Hudson-type steamer and the Preamble by an F-3.

Former Marketing Director Sam Bushala then scrapped the plans to make the Freedom Train in O gauge and instead decided to do it in HO. Lionel brought out the Preamble in O gauge with no matching cars. Many collectors ended up buying two units so they could display double-As on their shelves.

8566 SOUTHERN A
8567 DUMMY
8661 B UNIT

1975 through 1977. The Southern Railroad and its former president, W. Graham Claytor, have always been quite cooperative about sending Lionel pictures of its graphics. Claytor, now U.S. secretary of transportation, is a toy train enthusiast. Working from Southern-supplied material, Bill Diss and the Lionel engineering department came up with a version of the Southern F-3 that is closer to the prototype than the old Lionel version, which had no nose decoration.

One interesting aspect of the 8566 graphics is the Crescent marking on the front. That would normally designate that a Southern engine would be used for passenger service, but Lionel offered no cars with the Southern. Diss apparently has plans, however. "Perhaps we will bring out the aluminum cars in Southern markings someday," he says. "Wouldn't that make a nice set?"

The Southern B unit was introduced with the engine in 1975, the first time a B unit was introduced the same year as the A.

8562 SANTA FE
8563 DUMMY
8777 B UNIT

1976 and 1977. The 8562 Santa Fe has been the sleeper of the Fundimensions Era. Brought out in 1976 with little fanfare, less expectations, and still less anticipation on the part of the public, it has become one of the most sought after F-3 of the '70s.

Old Lionel's Santa Fe was introduced in 1948 and ran for 18 years. It was the most common of the F-3s. It was practically the most common *anything* that Lionel made. Collectors yawned when the new Lionel announced it was going to resurrect the Santa Fe.

Santa Fe F-3.

"We just made the Santa Fe because it is such a popular road name and such a beautiful color scheme," says Bill Diss. "Every toy train company eventually has to make a red and silver Santa Fe. The reason we waited so long was because we knew there were so many originals out there. We would be competing with old Lionel. Frankly, I didn't think it would sell very well."

The fact is, it did *not* cause much excitement at first. One of the reasons was that it did not look very interesting in the catalog. The Santa Fe shown in the catalog was not the one produced. At the time they made the catalog they did not yet have a mock-up of the new Santa Fe so they used an old one, the 2383, for the picture. Among other things, that model had black trucks.

When the 8562 came out it was, in the opinion of many collectors, the most beautiful engine to come out of Mount Clemens. It had painted silver trucks and crisp marking. The nose decal was larger and more elongated than the original and the frame as well as the trucks was painted silver. The simulated roof horns were made of cast metal, just like the originals, instead of the metalized plastic the other F-3s from Mount Clemens had. The intricate paint mask for the Santa Fe alone cost more than $9,000. Three ribs were added to the side of the plastic cab, running along the bottom, to aid in masking the three different colored stripes. The result is a decorating job that is better than the original. The only defect is that the rears of the A units have a tendency to crack where they are riveted to the brackets.

Once the engine was in the stores and collectors began to see what a fine piece it was, the demand grew until the supply can no longer meet it.

"I could sell 25 at a single meet, I get that many requests for it," says one dealer. Lionel so far has shown little evidence that they are aware of the commotion the Santa Fe has caused in collectors circles. Perhaps when they find out, they will make a reissue.

8851 NEW HAVEN
8852 DUMMY
8864 B UNIT

1978 and 1979. When the next year's line was being considered in 1977, Lionel executives decided to bring out a twin-motored F-3. It would be a high-priced item and they wanted to select a road name that would suggest quality. The New Haven was chosen because it was the most sought-after of the old Lionel F-3s that had not yet been ressurected.

Marketing had the idea to box the A and the dummy units together, selling an AA combination as a package. The New Haven was introduced in a spring, 1978, brochure and then included in the 1979 catalog. The orders were not overwhelming. The marketing technique of packaging engines as AA combinations is being reevaluated.

The 8851 has the same body as the 8562 Santa Fe, with the three ribs on the bottom of the cab.

The 8864 B unit may have a unique distinction. It may be the last B unit that Lionel will ever make. They made none for the 8952 Pennsylvania and intend to make none.

"We don't sell enough B units to make them worthwhile," says Marketing Manager Pete Sappenfield. "We were going to do B units for both Pennsys but those plans have been scrapped. No more B units are in the plans. They are not economically feasible to make any more. If we priced them to make them profitable they would be prohibitive."

8952 PENNSYLVANIA
8953 DUMMY

1979. The 8952 Pennsylvania F-3 is a nice piece. It is well detailed and well decorated. But it certainly has caused some controversy.

The first arguments began to swirl among collectors when the item was shown in the 1979 Toy Fair catalog. Also shown in that catalog were the new aluminum cars in Pennsylvania Tuscan red striping. Why, many collectors wanted to know, was the 8952, a separate sale item, painted in green, while the aluminum cars were Tuscan? Didn't the Lionel people know that many collectors would want to match the cars and the engine in a set, even if they were not offered as one?

It turned out the Lionel people were quite aware of the situation and, in fact, the whole issue had been a matter of much corporate debate. Their research had shown the real F-3s on the Pennsylvania were always used in freight service and no F-3 had ever been painted Tuscan, a passenger color. All the F-3s came in the green freight colors.

Final touch-up.

"It was a matter of accuracy," says Pete Sappenfield. "There were some of us who favored the Tuscan and some of us who favored the green. We were trying to find out if there were ever any Tuscan F-3s on the Pennsylvania. Finally we took it to the vice-president of public relations, who used to be with the Pennsylvania. He said the F-3s were green, so we went with green. It was a close decision. I think accuracy is more important than changing the correct color to make a matching set."

John Palm, one of the foremost experts on Lionel trains in the world, represents a school that takes strong exception to this argument.

"Here is a case where they should sacrifice a little accuracy to make a beautiful set. O.k., you can make a case that technically the passenger F-3 should be green. But why be so accurate here, and lose a matching set, then make a round window caboose with Chicago North Western markings. No one except the Pennsylvania ever used the round window caboose. No consistency."

Another collector points out that even though the PRR did not use F-3s for passenger service, it used F-7s and other F units to pull passenger cars. Many collectors just ignored the whole controversy. They simply bought the 8952 F-3 and put it at the head of a freight set and bought the aluminum cars and put them behind the 8753 maroon GG-1, making a new Congressional Set.

The next disturbance was caused when the 8952 was delivered to dealers. It was discovered that the window inserts were made of the same white opaque plastic that is used in passenger car windows. Howls immediately were heard. Many customers would not buy the engine unless the inserts were changed to clear plastic, as F-3s had always had. Some reluctantly bought the engine because they said it looked good lighted in darkness. Others didn't seem to care.

The opaque windows were apparently a mistake. According to Lionel sources, clear plastic window inserts were definitely intended, but a parts order was misread and somehow the mistake went unnoticed during assembly. This is easier to do than one might expect. A couple of renowned Lionel authorities, Tom McComas and James Tuohy, were at Plant 1 in Mount Clemens in the spring of 1979 when the Pennsylvania F-3s were being assembled. They didn't notice the opaque windows either, until they looked at pictures sometime later.

While Lionel mistakenly added opaque windows, they also added clear plastic portholes on the sides and plastic grab-irons on the front, a bit of additional detailing that met with great favor with collectors.

There is a postscript to the Great Green-Tuscan-Opaque-Clear controversy. In late 1979 Lionel brought out a Tuscan five-striper with clear windows.

"We yielded to the pressure," said Bill Diss.

RATING
1. 8365 Canadian Pacific
2. 8562 Santa Fe
3. 8466 Amtrak
4. 8566 Southern

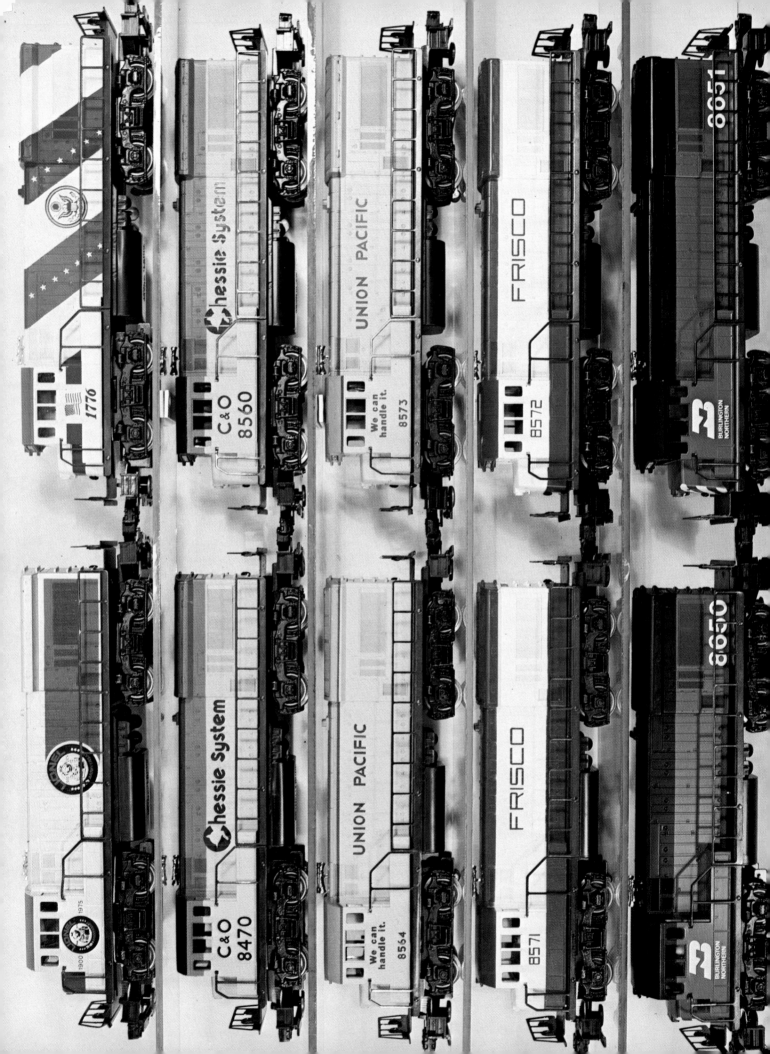

U36Bs & U36Cs

It took until 1974 before an engine casted from an all-new die was produced in Mount Clemens. It was the U36B. The year before Lionel had brought out the GP-20, an engine never made before, but that had required only minor adjustments on existing tooling. The idea for the U36B was Dick Branstner's, vice-president of engineering and development.

"We had received a lot of pressure from collectors to come out with some new loco-motives, something that Lionel had never made before," says Branstner. "I got the feeling from the collectors I talked with that a General Electric U-boat was what they wanted. Most everything else we had was General Motors."

Branstner sold the idea to George Toteff, the first president of Model Products Corporation. After getting the go-ahead from Toteff, Branst-ner contacted a Canadian toolmaker who cast the first model. It took six months.

"The model looked great so, we decided to tool it," says Branstner. "It cost around $30,000. It really should have been bigger but we made it fit the same frame we had because it would have cost too much to tool up for a whole new frame. I was making a toy. I didn't think about scale."

If it had been made to scale the U36B would have been longer than the FM. Other than the size, the U36B was a fine model. It used the same frame, trucks and motor as the geeps. Since it does share those features with the geeps, some collectors have wondered why the U36Bs are more expensive.

"There's more detail on the U-boats," says Bill Diss. "They cost us a lot more to decorate. Paint masks are elaborate because they have to fit over that radiator 'wing' on the end. The mask for the Southern Pacific cost about $5,000. Then, of course, we have the amortization of the costs of the new molds."

The first U36B was the Seaboard Coastline Bicentennial. It was introduced in August of 1974. The Chessie came out later that same year, in time for Christmas.

1776 SEABOARD COASTLINE "SPIRIT OF '76"

1974 through 1976. The Seaboard was the first railroad to have an engine painted in a Bicentennial theme. Lionel was eager to have a special issue of their own based on the Bi-

centennial and they rushed to get a model of the Seaboard into production. Perhaps in their eagerness they rushed too much. They forgot to put "Seaboard Coastline" on the sides of the frames, as it was on the prototype. Lionel received a letter from the Seaboard vice-president of public relations requesting the name be added. Bill Diss discussed it with Dick Branstner and the decision was made to add the lettering in mid-run, which is an unusual thing for Lionel to do.

"We wanted to be correct," says Diss, "even if it meant making a change after production had begun. Seaboard had been very coopera-tive and we felt we owed it to them."

Applying the lettering was difficult. The frame was unpainted black. "White over black is always a problem," says Diss, "especially when you are printing on an oily, oxidized sur-face. Sometime we had to triple-hit the frame to make the letters clear. If the frames had been painted black it would have been easier.

Frame being blackened.

The Seaboard was Lionel's first attempt to decorate a frame. At least three different shades of white have been reported. Lionel made a special version of the Spirit of '76 for the Train Collectors Association. On that model the frame was painted white and carried the TCA logo.

TCA U36B.

The Seaboard, which came out in August of 1974, was the first engine to have stamped metal handrails. Lionel broke its numbering system when it assigned the 1776 number to

the Seaboard, but that was the same number the real engine had. The real engine, however, was a U36C and had a frame that was painted blue, with four white stars on it.

8470 CHESSIE & 8560 DUMMY

1974. The Chessie, which was featured in the 1974 catalog pulling a top-of-the-line set, was a good model of the real Chessie U36B, but it has been the object of a minor complaint. The orange stripe on the 8470 is wider than the orange stripe on the 8463 GP-20 which came out the same year. Lionel had done well with the GP-20 Chessie and had decided to continue with the colorful paint scheme. Some collectors wanted to know why Lionel didn't continue it the exact same way.

"It's true they are different widths, but so are the stripes on the prototypes different," says Bill Diss. "The Chessie is one of the railroads that always cooperates with us and they sent us photos of both engines. Our models are accurate reproductions."

The 8560 dummy unit came out in 1975. It was illuminated. Some dummy units do not have the "C&O 8560" on the sides of the cab. This is an factory error.

Frames before blackening process.

7500 75TH ANNIVERSARY SPECIAL

1975 and 1976. The 75th Anniversary set, which it took two years for Lionel to unload, was pretty ugly. The decision to make it was made by Sam Bushala, the director of marketing, who rejected several other ideas, including one for a passenger set headed by a steam engine. The sides of the cars on that set would have shown the different logos Lionel used through the years.

Once again, Lionel broke its numbering system to give the 7500 number to the Anniversary Special U36B. It would seem that putting numbers such as "1776" and "7500" on these special engines would be a logical thing to do and apparently most collectors think so, but some think commemorative editions should be given regular sequential numbers, even if the other number is prominently displayed.

8564 UNION PACIFIC & 8573 DUMMY

1975. Lionel feels safe with names like Pennsylvania, Santa Fe, and Union Pacific, so they felt confident that a Union Pacific U36B would sell well. They were right.

The body of the model is an accurate reproduction of the UP's prototype, but Lionel used an unpainted black frame again. The Union Pacific does not have any black frames on its line. They are all gray, with a red stripe on them.

The 8573 dummy had the electronic horn in it, because some were left over when it was decided to discontinue that item on the GP-20s. A reported 1,200 horns were put in U36B dummies and this unit is difficult to find now. It is not illuminated. No Union Pacific U36B dummies were made without the horn.

Frames emerging from drying booth.

8650 BURLINGTON NORTHERN & 8651 DUMMY

1976 and 1977. The decision to make this engine contained no mysterious elements. It was a well-known railroad and it had rather stylish contemporary graphics. It did not sell well, which perhaps demonstrates that not everyone is excited about stylish contemporary graphics.

The Burlington Northern did not occupy a place of prominence in the 1976 catalog, its picture blending in with two pages of other engines, but Lionel gave it a big push the following year, or at least tried to. In 1977 they used it on a layout showing the workmanship that goes into making a Lionel engine — the cab detailing, the motor, the trucks, the frame, the E-unit. Unfortunately, this dissected model showed the cab of the 8651, the dummy unit, which would not have had all that stuff under its shell. How many people this display might have confused is not known, but anyway, Lionel got rid of all its leftover 8650s in 1977.

8571 FRISCO & 8572 DUMMY

1975 and 1976. As opposed to the Union Pacific, Lionel had reservations about doing the Frisco. It is a West Coast line and not particularly well known in other parts of the country. Lionel's biggest markets are in the East Coast and Midwest. However, the Frisco had a colorful paint scheme and the previous U36Bs had sold well, so the decision was made to make the 8571. Sales the first year were disappointing. It was cataloged again in 1976.

The dummy was introduced the same year as the powered unit. Until then the U36B dummies had been coming out a year after the powered unit.

Testing E-units.

8669 ILLINOIS CENTRAL GULF

1976. The main reason for making this engine was that the Illinois Central and the Gulf Mobile & Ohio had just completed their merger. Lionel wanted to be out quickly with a piece that would display the new graphics. It displayed them well. The 8669 headed a freight set which had a matching caboose. To get the engine and the caboose, the whole set had to be purchased. All the other items in the set could be purchased separately.

No dummy units for the 8669 were made.

8755 SANTA FE & 8756 DUMMY

1977 and 1978. When it was decided to do a Santa Fe U36B, engineering administrator Bill Diss assigned a number to it. Then he wrote to the Santa Fe requesting a photograph of a U36B so that Lionel could copy the graphics. When the photograph arrived, Diss noticed that the U36B pictured had the number 8755. That was not the number Diss had assigned to Lionel's Santa Fe, but it was close enough that he decided to use it. The number

Photo sent to Lionel by the Santa Fe Railroad.

8755 had already been assigned to another Lionel engine, but Diss did some quick juggling of numbers and came up with a model that not only matched its prototype in graphics, but in number.

8771 GREAT NORTHERN

1977. The engine was featured in the catalog at the head of the Rocky Mountain Special. It was a pretty fair model of the prototype Great Northern, except that the real engine has a charcoal gray roof and the Lionel version has a black roof. The Great Northern is a traditional road name and has a well-known goat-in-a-circle herald and the name and the herald appeared on the engine, but nobody is very interested in it for some reason. Everybody wants the cars in the set, but the engine has inspired only ennui among collectors. Lionel did not bother to make a dummy.

8857 NORTHERN PACIFIC & 8858 DUMMY

1978. This was the first engine to have the handrails on each end be part of the stamping, so that the entire frame, with the exception of the side rails, is now a one-piece stamp. Before, the end rails were put on by riveting them to the frame.

8773 MICKEY MOUSE

1977. See SETS.

8955 SOUTHERN & 8956 DUMMY

1979. The Southern Railroad uses a high-nosed version of the U36B. Lionel has no high-nosed U36B dies, but it wanted to make a Southern U36B. It made it in a low-nosed version. Some collectors criticized Lionel for its ignorance. It wasn't ignorance.

"I knew the Southern only used high-nosed U36Bs," says Bill Diss, who made the decision to make the Southern. "I took the liberty. After all, we're making toys."

Southern cabs before final assembly.

Diss took another liberty. Southern's road diesels are painted black with white trim and gold lettering. Lionel's is painted green instead of black, like the Southern F-3.

Paint spray booth.

8960 SOUTHERN PACIFIC U36C & 8961 DUMMY

1979. The difference between the "B" and the "C" lettering on General Electric U-boats is that the Bs have four-wheel trucks and the Cs six-wheel. To make the Southern Pacific a C, Lionel took the six-wheel trucks developed in 1978 for the SD-18 and put it on the U36.

Packaging of Southern Pacific sets.

The Southern Pacific U36C was introduced as part of a Limited Edition set in a flyer at the 1979 Toy Fair. The set included the 8961 dummy and six cars, none of which were to be sold separately. Included in the cars was the gold bullion car, which is a remake of the old Lionel car. The set, which is destined to become a favorite with collectors, was shown on the cover of the regular 1979 catalog, but by that time it was not available for sale. The entire Limited Edition run had been sold out in the spring.

RATING

1. 8573 Union Pacific Dummy
2. 1776 TCA Bicentennial
3. 8564 Union Pacific powered
4. 8773 Mickey Mouse
5. 8669 Illinois Central Gulf

Chessie U36B prototype.

SD-18

EMD's SD-18 is essentially a lengthened version of the GP-9 with a bulge over the radiator at the end of the hood. It has more horsepower and rides on six-wheel trucks rather than four. The Lionel model, which came out in 1978, was essentially its GP-20 with new six-wheel trucks and a new bell and simulated horn on the roof and shorter belly tanks.

"It cost us $110,000 to retool the SD-18," says Fundimensions President Jim Boosales. "Just to make new trucks and slightly change the GP-20 body."

Almost all of that money went for the trucks, which are of a completely new casting. They are good models of the EMD three-motored Flexicoil truck. Both the power trucks and dummy are die-cast. The side frames are also die-cast. They are designed to fit the same mounting pocket in the frame that the four-wheel trucks fit. Since the GP-7s, -9s, -20s, and U-36Bs all use the same frame, any one of them can take the new trucks.

The fuel tank is shorter, to make room for the new trucks. It also drops down lower, giving it a more beefy look. The coupler system was cheapened considerably, to the same plastic, snap-on type used on the boxcars. The old ones had more metal in them and a better armature plate. Besides costing less, the new ones required less assembly time. The motor, frame, and dynamic brake blister are the same as those on the GP-9. They have the one-piece chassis with the handrails bent up on the ends.

The SD-18, while not as heavy as it could be, is nevertheless a good puller. "There's plenty of power there," says collector Jason Stern of Chicago. "We were pulling 22 of the old Lionel cars with one SD-18, so that's pretty good."

The first SD-18 was the 8855 Milwaukee Road. It headed a top-of-the-line freight set, The Milwaukee Limited, in the 1978 catalog. No dummy was made for the 8855.

The 8872 Santa Fe was first shown in a Fall, 1978, flyer. Like the Milwaukee Road, the Santa Fe had graphics that were excellent

reproductions of the original. It had silver side frames. The 8872 was offered as part of a "Year-end Special." The Year-end Special is an interesting Lionel marketing strategy that belies the company's claim that Lionel "is not in the business of creating collectors items" (see HISTORY, page 14).

The Year-end Special has been offered every year since 1974. It is a package to dealers that includes, as an example, $800 worth of merchandise for $600, but in the package will be many things the dealer does not particularly want. It is a way for Lionel to unload some surplus stock. A typical Year-end Special may include a gross of switches and a gross of telephone poles, but then also six engines, six dummies and six matching cabooses, all from the upcoming year's line. That gives the dealer — as in the case of the 8872 Santa Fe SD-18 — a chance to sell next year's item the previous Christmas. He can then test public reaction to the item before ordering from the spring catalog. But the biggest enticement in the Year-end Special is a car Lionel makes only for this package.

The special car is almost guaranteed to become a collectors item because of the limited number of them made. Each package has four of the special cars in it, but probably only one-quarter of the dealers take advantage of the deal, not wanting to put out the cash for all the other stuff they have to take. The Year-end Special cars for the first five years were: 1974, the 9757 Central of Georgia boxcar; 1975, the 7700 Uncle Sam boxcar; 1976, the 9780 Johnny Cash boxcar; 1977, the 7803 Trains 'N Truckin boxcar; 1978, the 9672 Mickey Mouse 50th birthday hi-cube boxcar; 1979, a boxcar with heralds from the Great American railroads series. All these cars were sold at up to ten times the price of a normal new boxcar.

Besides the Mickey Mouse car in the 1978 deal, the Lionel dealers received a bonus, the red 9274 Santa Fe caboose. This car is destined to become a collectors item, and that story is told in the CABOOSE section.

5 Milwaukee
　Road
2 Santa Fe
3 Santa Fe
2 Santa Fe with
　number omitted

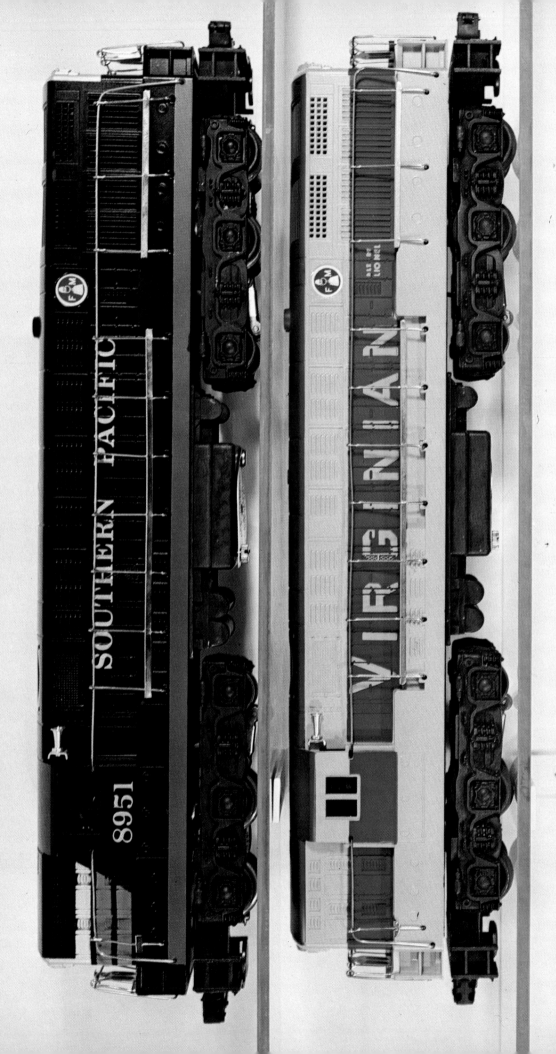

FM UNITS

When, in the fall of 1978, the word was out that Lionel planned to do an FM Trainmaster, TM Productions of Wilmette, Illinois, contacted Lionel and asked for a color photograph of one. TM Productions puts out a toy train calendar every year and they wanted to include the new FM in their 1979 calendar. Lionel didn't have a picture.

John Brady, Lionel's assistant products manager, explained that plans called for Lionel to make a Virginian and Southern Pacific, but that prototypes of those two models would not be available until January, so a photograph could not be taken until then. That would be too late for TM's production schedule.

Brady sent Tom McComas a rough sketch of the SP model Lionel planned to do. It was like the version that was eventually made except it did not have the orange stripe along the bottom of the frame. McComas had remembered seeing that stripe on a prototype model that the old Lionel engineering department had made up in the 1950s but that had never been put into production. That prototype is now in the collection of LaRue Shempp, who has one of the greatest Lionel collections in existence. A fine photograph of that engine appeared in *Toy Train Treasury, Vol. 2* (Iron Horse Productions, 1975) a book on the Shempp Collection. McComas sent a copy of the photograph to Brady, who decided to include the orange stripe on the Lionel model.

The models were used for pictures in the catalog. However, in the catalog picture the Virginian cab was on backwards, as the cabs are in both models on the opposite page. It is a minor point, but the cab end of the FM shell should be closer to the single air tank on the chassis than the double air tanks. The shell fits on the chassis either way.

During the toy shows Lionel was surprised at the way the orders came in.

"We figured the Southern Pacific would outsell the Virginian by a wide margin," says Brady. "We figured most collectors already have the original so they will think twice before buying the Mount Clemens versions. But the Virginian sold more than we thought. Our records so far indicate a very slight preference for the S.P., but nowhere near as great as we had anticipated."

The final ratio was four SPs sold for every three Virginians, but the most interesting aspect of the reissued FMs was that by the fall of 1979 there were not enough of either engine to meet the demand.

It turned out that Lionel, although it never announced the fact in the spring of 1979, decided to make both the SP and Virginian Limited Edition items. That meant that no more than the original runs would ever be made. This was both unneccesarily irritating and confusing to the buying public.

"By rights we should have announced it was going to be a Limited Edition when we announced the engine," says Pete Sappenfield. "It was just a matter of being rushed for the catalog deadline and at that time we had not decided whether or not to make it a Limited Edition. But the more of the FMs I saw, and how nice they were turning out, I just thought they should be Limited Editions. We will have more orders than we can fill but we will make more FMs in the future. Not the Virginian or SP but other road names. I think the demand is for a Lionel FM, not necessarilly a Virginian or SP. Eventually the demand will be filled."

The first FM scheduled to appear after the Virginian and SP was a green and yellow Chicago & North Western, planned for the 1980 line. It would come with a matching bay window caboose.

C&NW FM unit.

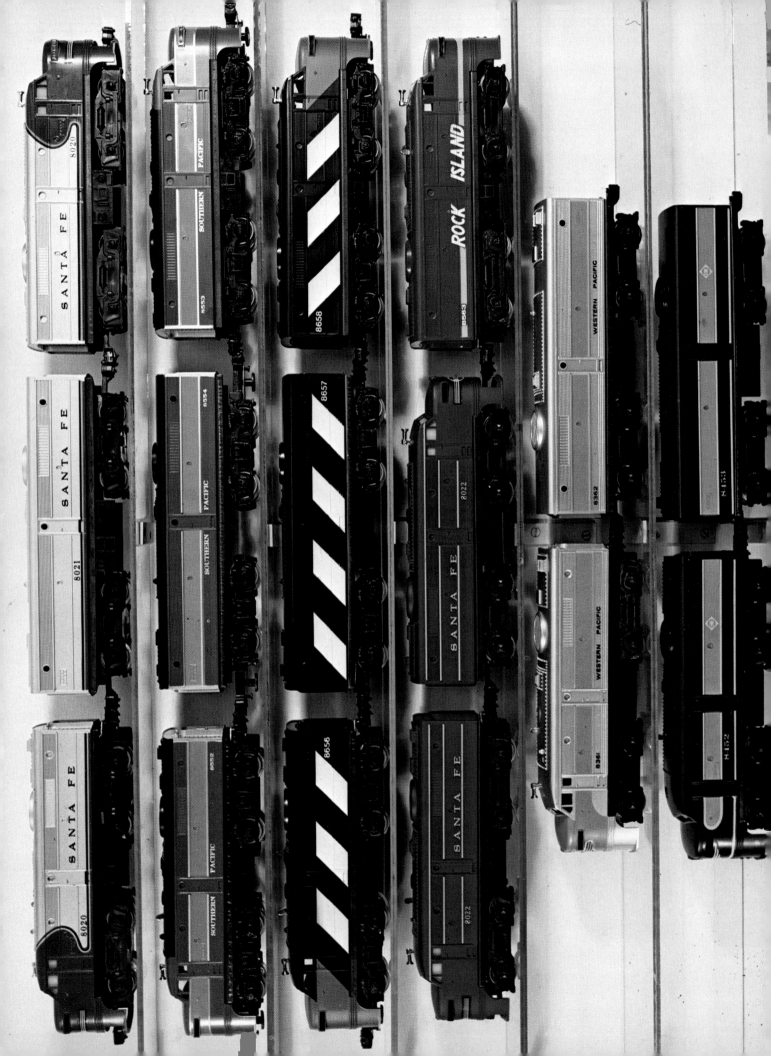

ALCOS

8020 Santa Fe
8553 Southern Pacific
8658 CN
8563 Rock Island

The first Lionel model of an Alco FA appeared in 1950. It was a medium-priced, undersized version of the real FAs but it had a quiet, smooth-running motor that many collectors feel is the best Lionel ever made. Although the proportions were wrong, the detailing on the Alco was good and it had a die-cast frame and trucks.

The original version of the Alco ran through 1954, then it was cheapened. The motor was changed to a one-piece motor-truck assembly which was not as smooth or efficient as the one it replaced. Body detailing was reduced and the frame was stamped sheet metal. Its total look compared to the original was rather cheap and for that reason collectors pretty much ignored Alcos made after 1954, even though quite a few road names were issued in the 1950s and 1960s.

8021 Santa Fe
8554 Southern Pacific
8657 CN
8022 Santa Fe
8362 Western Pacific
8453 Erie

The Alco of the Fundimension era is similar to the cheapened version of the '60s. Mechanically it is adequate because it has the same motor that the geep does. Graphically it is better. "Some of the paint jobs are gorgeous," says one collector, "but the overall look is still cheap."

"We can't afford to have everything top-of-the-line," says Lionel's Bill Diss. "We have to have some mid-range diesels and the Alco is the obvious choice because they are not really very close to the prototype. The geeps are good copies of the prototypes, so we want those to be among our top engines. I think the Alco is a good quality engine for our mid-range sets."

However, since the Alco is not a top-flight model, Diss admits that in his opinion some nice paint schemes have been wasted on them. "I thought marketing was crazy when they used the Southern Pacific Daylight colors on an Alco. I have been trying to get an F-3 done in that scheme for a long time. It helped that the Alco daylight came in a nice long ABA combination and used die-cast trucks, but it was still a waste. I never would have used the Canadian National on the Alcos either. I still plan to have an F-3 made in Daylight colors."

8020 Santa Fe
8552 Southern Pacific
8656 CN
8022 Santa Fe
8361 Western Pacific
8452 Erie

The first of the new Alcos, the 8020 Santa Fe and the uncataloged 8022 J. C. Penney, had filled-marker boards, and a large cut-out in the front pilot. Die-cast truck frames were added in 1972 to give the engine some traction. The large opening on the pilot was filled in, except on the higher priced version, which came with front couplers and three-position reverse units. The cheaper version had no coupler and two-position or manual reverse. From 1972 through 1979 only the Southern Pacific and Canadian National ABAs came in the higher-priced version.

Bernie Puralewski, co-editor of *The Lion Roars,* is an Alco fan and feels they will eventually increase in value, "I think the Alcos are a good place for the new collectors to start. They make a very attractive assortment and some are hard to find. Lower-priced items like the steamers and Alcos were generally ignored by collectors and those that were sold were sold to kids and destroyed. The higher-priced items were bought by collectors and are plentiful. That's why lower-priced categories present a much greater challenge from a collecting standpoint."

Here are some brief notes on the more desirable Alcos.

8656 CANADIAN NATIONAL
8657 B UNIT, 8658 DUMMY

1976. The dummy A unit is very hard to find. Bill Diss explains. "We didn't sell as many as we anticipated so we made powered units out of some of the units that were earmarked to be dummy units. That's why there are fewer dummies."

8022 SANTA FE

1970. Uncataloged. Sold in a set through the J. C. Penney stores. Some sets came with single A unit and some sets came with double-A units. The first 8022s made used left-over cabs that were repainted blue.

8552 SOUTHERN PACIFIC
8553 B UNIT, 8554 DUMMY

1975 and 1976. The Southern Pacific scheme is very colorful and proved to be a good seller. Collectors feel that if the engine had come with matching 027 streamline passengers cars it would have been even a bigger seller.

8563 ROCK ISLAND

1975. Uncataloged. This engine headed a freight set that was sold through Sears.

RATING

1. 8656 Canadian National ABA
2. 8022 Santa Fe AA (J. C. Penney)
3. 8552 Southern Pacific ABA
4. 8563 Rock Island (Sears)
5. 8025 CN AA

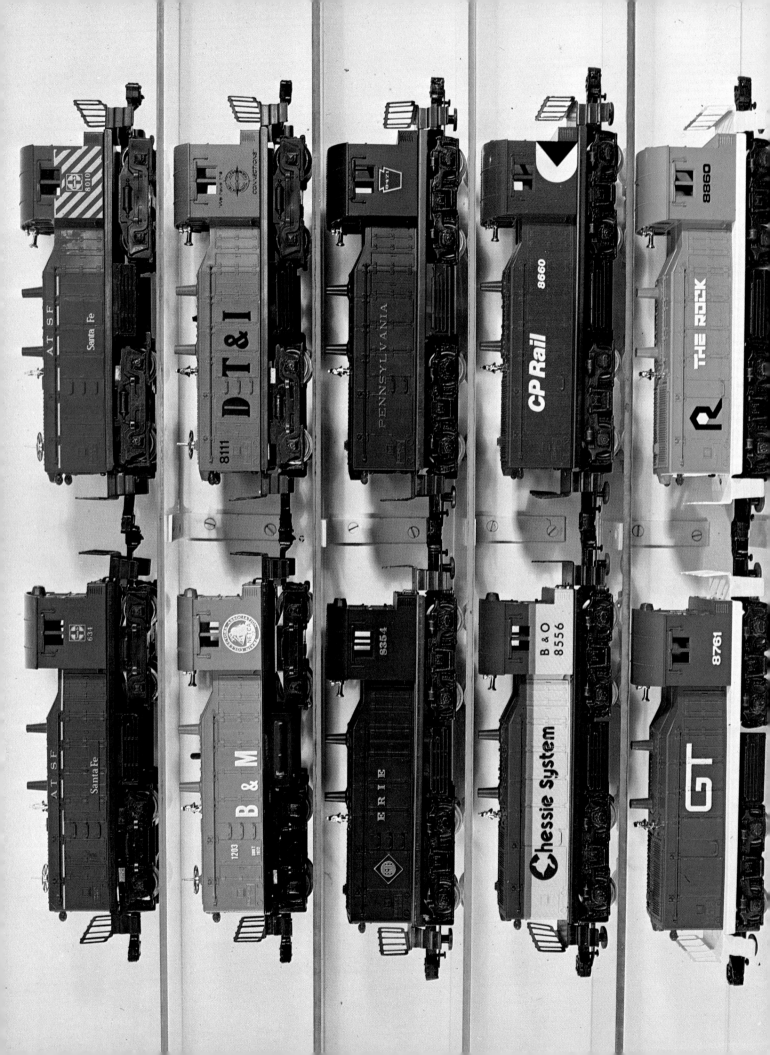

SWITCHERS

8010 Santa Fe
8111 DT&I
8471 Pennsylvania
8660 CP Rail
8860 The Rock

The NW-2 switcher (see Volume II for the difference between the SW and NW prototype switchers) followed the same course as the Alcos. The original versions, introduced in 1949, had a cast frame, wire handrails, and the same smooth-running motor that the Alcos had. This switcher was cheapened in 1955 when the frame was stamped.

The Lionel version introduced in 1970 is very similar to the old, cheapened version. The motor is the same as that used in the geeps and, like the Alcos, the graphics are excellent. Some collectors feel that if Lionel put their new, handsome cab on a die-cast frame they would have a hot-seller on their hands. Lionel doesn't think so.

"If you make improvements on the frame and add wire handrails then the price is driven up about even with the geeps and U36Bs," says Bill Diss. "When you get that high, people are going to buy the road diesels rather than the switchers. Considering the cost limitations we have to work with, I think the switchers are pretty nice models. The Chessie, Rock and CP Rail are all good, colorful paint schemes. The unfortunate thing about the switchers is they don't sell well."

There are no switchers planned for the 1980 line, but that does not mean Lionel will discontinue them completely. About every railroad in the country had one of these switchers, so potential roadnames certainly are not lacking.

Here are some of the more sought-after switchers.

8010 SANTA FE

1970. There are two versions. One has yellow stripes running along the side of the cab. The other does not have the yellow stripes. The version with the stripes is harder to find.

634 SANTA FE

1970. This is the same engine as the 8010, only with the old Lionel number on it. It even came in a box that said 8010 on it. What happened was that Mount Clemens inherited some leftover 634 Santa Fe bodies from the old regime. Mount Clemens put the new horn and radio antenna on them — as they did on the 8010 — but did not bother to change the old number.

634 Santa Fe
1203 TCA B&M
8354 Erie
8556 Chessie System
8761 Grand Trunk

There are two types of 634 bodies. One is all blue with yellow lettering and the other is blue with yellow lettering and yellow stripes on the cab. All the 634s were early switchers. After all the old cabs were used, Lionel began putting the 8010 number on the switchers. The 634 can be faked by putting an original 634 body on an MPC frame and adding the trim. As a matter of fact, that's precisely how Mount Clemens made it. The reason collectors sometimes try to fake the new 634 is because it's the most valuable of all the Mount Clemens switchers.

8473 COCA COLA

1974 and 1975. The Coke switcher came with a manual reverse and non-operating couplers. Variations exist having to do with the number of steps on the side of the cab. There are one-step, two-step and three-step versions. For more on the "Coke Set" see SETS.

8556 CHESSIE

1975 and 1976. Lionel decided to spend an unusual amount of money for decorating a switcher to see what kind of response they received. The paint masks were expensive because three colors were involved and the switcher body has a lot of detail. The Chessie was an artistic success but its sales record was disappointing.

1203 BOSTON & MAINE

Uncataloged. Lionel made this engine for the Train Collectors Association and it bares a TCA notation on the side of the body.

8860 THE ROCK

1978 and 1979. "The Rock was nicely designed and that big R fit perfectly into one of the panels on the side of our model," explained Bill Diss. "I liked the color too."

SMALL SWITCHERS

Lionel made three gas-turbine switchers that were sold in starter sets and had DC motors. They are shown in the picture on page 120. These small switchers are cheaply made and are ignored by collectors.

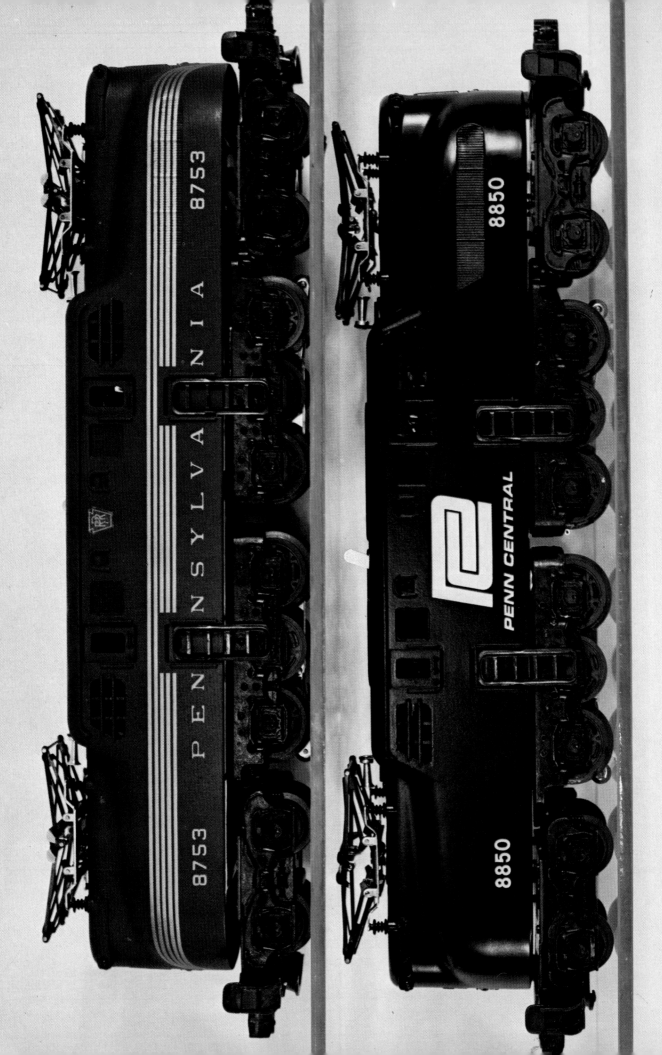

ELECTRICS

GG-1s

When General Mills began making Lionel trains, three engines immediately became top choices among collectors for reissue. They were the Hudson, Norfolk & Western, and GG-1. The GG-1 came back in the spring of 1977 when an advertising flyer announced plans to make "one of the great classics of the past." As 1980 approached, collectors were still hoping for the Hudson and Norfolk & Western.

8753 PENNSYLVANIA

1977. The first GG-1 to appear since 1963 was painted a flat wine with Pennsy markings and five gold stripes. "Getting the stripes on was a problem for us," explains Bill Diss, "Old Lionel did it a completely different way than we did. They applied the stripes with a rubber stamp, using gold leaf. Everyone knows these stripes rubbed off easily. We could have done it the same way but we wanted to improve on that rub-off situation. We used a dry-transfer for the stripes, then covered the whole thing with clear lacquer. We received criticism because our lines did not merge as well as the original. They came to a blob rather than a point. We were criticized for the rough finish, too. I think the complaints are legitimate. We should have done a better job."

The selling price of the GG-1 is another thing that some collectors are not happy with. "The whole thing except for the body is available in parts for just over $100," reports one collector. "I know, because I had an extra body and at York last year I bought the power trucks for $30 each, the two dummy trucks for $10 each, the frame was $5, reverse units about $7 and the pantographs $6 each. That's the whole thing right there."

"There's always guys playing the angles," says Lenny Dean, whose job is to supply parts to service stations. "If you want to justify the cost of the parts versus the cost of the engine, the difference is all in the cab and we are not selling the cab. If the total for parts is low on a particular engine its because we don't sell the cab. If we did sell the cab then that $30 power truck would have to be $90. We price our parts low as a service to those who need parts. Not so some guy can put the engine together."

Lionel does sell some cabs but they want the old cab back before the new one is sent out.

"I think they let the prices the original GG-1s are selling for influence them when they priced the new GG-1. No way that engine should cost over $200," says another collector.

Mechanically the new GG-1 is almost identical to the original. Most collectors are happy with the quality but there are complaints. The new version uses the same tapered wheels for the pilots that are used on rolling stock and that are attached to a "live axle" which turns with the wheels. On the original GG-1, the wheels were straight cut, not tapered, and they turned around a fixed axle. The tapered wheels of the pilot wobble down the tracks.

The problem can be eliminated by inserting the wheels and axle from any old Lionel freight car into the new pilots. Use a large-bladed screwdriver and carefully pry apart the sides of the trucks.

Other problems: The worm-gear shaft of the armature is too long. A hole had to be drilled into the bottom of the gearbox to accommodate the shaft. Consequently, the bottom of the worm-shaft is exposed and can pick up dirt. Also, excess grease leaks out and gets all over the third rail.

The new GG-1s are good pullers but not as good as the originals because the Magne-Traction is not as strong. The originals came with white rubber insulators that looked much better than the black plastic insulators the new ones come with. There is no horn in the new GG-1.

The 8753 was a Limited Edition model, meaning only one run was made and no other one ever will be.

8850 PENN CENTRAL

1978 and 1979. The Penn Central was announced the same way the Pennsylvania five-striper was, in a spring flyer. The Penn Central cost about $50 more than the 8753 and the only change was that the Penn Central had metal wheel gears and the Pennsylvania had nylon.

The Penn Central did not sell as fast as the Pennsylvania. Six thousand of each were made, according to Fundimensions President Jim Boosales, but some dealers thought that more Penn Centrals were made.

"The Penn Central moved slower than the Pennsy," answers assistant marketing manager John Brady. "We had some left over and we knew dealers did too, so we included it in the 1979 catalog."

OTHER ELECTRICS

RECTIFIERS

8659 VIRGINIAN

1976. General Electric built this 3,300 horsepower electric especially for the Virginian Railway.

Lionel's original version came out in 1958 and never sold well. Because of that, it became a prized collectors piece. When, in 1976, rumors began to circulate that Lionel was going to reissue the Virginian, originals began popping up on tables at meets all over the country. They were sold, those that were sold at all, at prices lower than before the reissue talk began. Many collectors were happy about this, feeling that the ugly rectifier was priced too high, anyway.

Lionel's model, like its EP-5, would have to have been longer and have six-wheel trucks to match the prototype. The new version was an improvement over the original. The paint was glossier and the markings more crisp. It had the F-3 trucks and a two-step pilot rather than the original's three-step. The new version has a shorter belly tank. There are operating couplers at both ends, but no horn or Magne-Traction.

Lionel made a hopper, boxcar and caboose to go with the new Virginian. All were available separately.

Some variations have been reported. They have to do with the nose decal. Some are dark yellow, some light yellow, and some are wider than others.

8754 NEW HAVEN

1977. The New Haven had the one-piece, bent handrails, while the Virginian had the old separately welded railings. The reverse unit bracket was altered, too. On the Virginian it had been a separate piece. On the New Haven the bracket was punched out of the frame.

Although by the time Lionel made the New Haven that railroad had been taken over by Conrail, Lionel executives decided to go with the old paint scheme. Besides the Virginian and New Haven, the only road to use the rectifier was the Pennsylvania. Lionel has hinted it may make a Pennsy rectifier some day.

EP-5s

Lionel's model of the EP-5 is a good one, except that the real engine had six-wheel trucks instead of the four-wheel Blomberg trucks that

are on the toy. The new EP-5s use the same power and dummy trucks as the F-3s. They have no horn or Magne-Traction. The battery box is plastic, rather than die-cast as it was on the original. They are illuminated, with operating couplers at both ends.

8551 PENNSYLVANIA

1975. Lionel decided not to bring the stripes to a point at the nose of the cab, as had been done on the original, because it is very hard to do.

There was a change made during the run having to do with the way the rivets secured the mounting clip to the body. On the first units made, the area where the rivet went through was recessed so the top of the rivet would not be higher than the surface of the body. This recession resulted in a thin area that weakened the body and the body cracked. So they stopped recessing the body. This made it stronger but the rivet stuck out above it. Now the rivet is visible even when a decal is applied over it.

Many operators use the Pennsy electric to pull the Broadway Limited passenger cars because the engine the cars came with does not do justice to the cars.

8558 MILWAUKEE ROAD

1976. Many collectors feel Lionel's choice of colors the second time around on the Milwaukee Road was much better than the first. The original Little Joe was painted yellow, black and maroon. The new version is orange, black and maroon. These are Olympian colors and a big improvement. Some operators use this engine to pull the Milwaukee Special cars, for the same reason they use the Pennsy to pull the Broadway Limited cars.

The 8558 designation is an exception to the rule. Usually the second digit of the engine's number is the same as the year the item was produced.

8762 GREAT NORTHERN

1977. This engine was almost identical to the original version except for two little Great Northern heralds next to the doors on the side. Like the other electrics, the 8762 did not break any sales records.

"For some reason, other than the GG-1, electrics are not good sellers," says Bill Diss.

Of the three that were made, the Great Northern commands the most attention.

STEAMERS
LARGE

The large steamers made in the 1970s were essentially remakes of the small Hudson-type steamers (655 and 2055, and 646 and 2046) made by Lionel in the 1950s. The original versions had Magne-Traction and whistles. Of the new versions four had Magne-Traction and three had a whistle. Most of the new versions used rubber tires to increase traction.

One feature the new steamers had that the old steamers did not was the "Mighty Sound of Steam." Sound of Steam was developed by Dick Branstner in 1970, and was considered by him a successful innovation. "I think it sold a lot of engines," he says. Most collectors feel that the Sound of Steam was the best new feature on Lionel engines since smoke.

Generally, the top-of-the-line steamers through the years varied little if at all. None of them is particularly rare either.

Steamer motor display.

8206 NEW YORK CENTRAL 4-6-4

1972 through 1975. This engine was cataloged in 1970 with the number 8062 and the road name Great Northern. It was never actually made with that number or that name. The first time it was made was in 1972 with NYC markings and the 8206 number. It was the first steamer with a six-wheel drive mechanism to be made in Mount Clemens. It used the old 665 die-cast boiler, had plastic trailing trucks, was painted flat black with white lettering and came with smoke and Sound of Steam.

An unusual feature of the 8206 was its Baldwin disk drive wheels. The last engine to use Baldwin drivers was the 675 made in 1949.

The 8206 was one of the engines to come with a whistle. It was similar to the electronic whistle that was used in the diesels (see GP-20 section). Unfortunately the control unit for the whistle was faulty and it caused static and background noises in the Sound of Steam unit. Instead of perfecting the control unit the whistle was dropped after the 8206 was discontinued. None of the other steamers had it. Some collectors, although not the majority, liked the whistle more than the Sound of Steam and would have preferred Lionel to have either perfected the whistle control unit or dropped the Sound of Steam.

8600 NEW YORK CENTRAL 4-6-4

1976. This was the old postwar 646-2046 Hudson. The 8600 headed the Empire State Express set. It was the biggest steam engine the new Lionel had made up to that time and it was later used for the 8702 Southern Crescent and the 8801 Blue Comet. It had Sound of Steam and smoke.

The 646-type engine had been considered back in 1972 to head the Milwaukee Special, which was the first set to use the new old-style passenger cars. They even had a prototype made with the number 8305 on it, as the photo below shows.

8305 Prototype.

The prototype was made in Hillside, New Jersey, but eventually it was decided that the 646-type steamer would cost more to produce than the company was at that time willing to spend. They used a smaller engine to head the 1973 Milwaukee Limited Set and gave the number 8305 to it.

Until the Empire State Express hit the market, it had been Lionel's policy to make available for separate sale all items in a set. The items in the Empire State Express were not sold separately. That switch in policy has caused the Empire State Express to become the most sought-after large steamer set of the 1970s.

Attaching side rods to drive wheels.

8603 CHESAPEAKE & OHIO 4-6-4

1976 and 1977. The 8603 was the same engine as the 8206 except for the boiler front. The 8603 used the same boiler front, painted silver, that was used on the old 646. It had the Baldwin disk drivers that the 8206 had. It was Bill Diss's idea to paint the boiler front silver. "We had been making the drab 8206 and I started to pester marketing to make a steamer that would have more appeal. When we decided to come out with the 8603 I said, Let's paint the boiler front and put whitewalls on the wheels and a stripe along the side."

Lionel did paint the boiler front silver but the other decoration was achieved by blackening the zinc wheels then grinding off the outside rim, making the wheel appear to have whitewalls. This was not a good idea because the unprotected metal eventually tarnished and pitted. The edge of the running board was also ground to give the effect of striping in 1976. It was painted in 1977.

The lettering on the tender came in white, even though it was shown in gold in the 1976 catalog.

Machines used to test unattached E-units.

The painting of the boiler front and the striping and whitewalls were important steps for Lionel. They would evenually lead to much more intricate decoration on the steamers.

The 8603 came with Sound of Steam and smoke.

8701 THE GENERAL 4-4-0

1977 through 1979. The real General engine belonged to the Western & Atlantic Railroad at the time of the outbreak of the civil war, April 12, 1861. The General was pressed into service in the Confederate cause, but a year to the day after the war began, on April 12, 1862, Union troops raided a Confederate unit and stole the General. The Rebels chased the Yankees in another Confederate engine, the Texas. The dramatic episode became the subject of a Walt Disney film, "The Great Locomotive Chase."

Lionel made a model of the General back in 1959. That set came with a baggage-mail car, a flatcar with horses, and a passenger car. The new Lionel General came with the same consist, but the 8701 locomotive was painted a different color from the original, which was gray and red with gold trim. The new one was black and red. The prototype General engine, the one that was used in the Civil War, was restored by the Louisville & Nashville Railroad and is now on display at a museum 25 miles north of Atlanta. The railroad sent pictures to Bill Diss and based on those the black and red color scheme was selected.

Steamer castings as they come from vendor.

"We checked the toolings for the General," says Diss, "and found it was in good shape, so we could make it just like the old one. The only thing we did differently was to add a smoke screen over the smokestack, change the drivers and pickups, and, of course, the color."

The original General came in Super O and 027. The Super O had everything — Magne-Traction, illumination, smoke. The 027 did not have smoke or Magne-Traction or operating couplers, but the new 8701 has all those things except Magne-Traction. A picture of the whole set is shown in SETS.

8702 SOUTHERN CRESCENT 4-6-4

1977 and 1978. The prototype Southern Crescent steamer was a 4-6-2 Pacific-type, but when Lionel decided to make a model of the Crescent it selected a small Hudson of the old 646-2046-type. Mount Clemens had the tooling to make a Pacific from the old 675 of the 1950s, but made the Hudson because that tooling was already restored. "It would have been a problem resurrecting all the tools needed for the original Pacific," says Bill Diss. "The Hudson cabbing is very similar to the prototype even if the wheel arrangement is not."

Testing motors.

Diss had seen a black and white photograph of the prototype and had written Southern President Graham Claytor for a color photograph. Claytor sent back the photograph shown below, from which Diss and the art department reproduced the color scheme. The Southern Railroad was known for its beautifully maintained steam power and its exquisite paint jobs. Lionel worked hard to accurately reproduce the distinctive "Virginia Green" that the Southern used and its detailed decoration.

"It was the most elaborate paint scheme for a steamer we had ever attempted," says Diss. "We put decoration on the engine and tender where decoration had never been before. If you want to be picky you could say the cab roof should be maroon and the area under the walkway should be black, but the real Crescent steamers came both ways — with the roof green or maroon and the area under the walkway green or black. There is a Southern Crescent in the Smithsonian Institute and it's not painted black under the walkway."

Lionel, learning from the experience of the 8603 C & O, decided to paint the whitewalls on the Crescent rather than grind the wheels. The total look of the 8702 was one of class, an appropriate model for a distinguished prototype. Collectors were unanimous in their praise of the 8702, some saying it was the best-looking steamer Lionel ever made, postwar or prewar.

Blue Comet motor with whitewall drivers.

The Crescents that came out in 1977 were painted a semi-gloss. When the passenger cars came out the next year they were glossy, so Lionel started painting the engines a glossy green. That meant that some collectors would have a semi-gloss engine they bought in 1977 and a glossy set of cars. Some traded engines to get a matched set.

8801 BLUE COMET 4-6-4

1978. The Standard gauge Blue Comet is, of course, one of the most popular trains among collectors that Lionel ever made. Some think it is the finest looking, too, and it is natural that talk about making a Blue Comet at Mount Clemens started early.

"I know we were talking about it back in 1973," says Bill Diss. "But somehow or other it got put on a back burner while we were preoccupied with other things." Then one day in 1976 a man showed up at the customer service entrance at the side of Lionel's Plant No. 1. He had a Standard gauge Blue Comet set of cars in good condition. They were headed by a black 392E. He wanted to know if anybody wanted to buy it. Diss was called.

"We didn't have a Blue Comet set in the archives," says Diss, "I offered him $1,000 for it. I told him a collector might offer him more but that's how much we could pay. He said o.k. I put the set in my office and after that I began to think about bringing out a Blue Comet again. I wrote to the Jersey Central, but they weren't very helpful. I needed some more information on the color scheme. I'm a stickler for realism. I want colorful trains — colorful trains are what sell — but they have to be prototypical. I just won't make up a train like Lionel did in the prewar days, for instance, with their Red Comet."

Paint touching-up of Blue Comets.

Diss found the information he needed in a *Trains* magazine article after writing Lynn Wescott, editor of *Trains*, and asking for help.

"He sent me an article from June of 1956 that had all kinds of pictures of the Blue Comet. Even though the pictures were black and white the copy described the color accurately. There were close-up shots of the boiler front, side views of the whole engine and good shots of the tender. After looking at those pictures I had a good idea of what the real Blue Comet was like."

Blue Comets in mobile racks.

The mask for the Blue Comet was intricate and cost about $5,000. "It was about like making another tool," says Diss. "You have to engrave all that detail that is on the boiler into the mask so it fits snug and makes a crisp line."

Some collectors did not like the glossy paint job of the Blue Comet. Diss defends it, although he admits that there has been a debate among the Lionel management over glossy-versus-dull paint schemes. "When real trains are new they are shiny," says Diss. "We are selling new models of real trains. We're not selling weathered trains. I don't think the Comet would have been as attractive with dull or semi-gloss paint. If collectors want to weather them they can."

The 8801 is the same engine as the 8702 Southern Crescent (they are both the old 646-2046 Hudsons), but the Comet has a modified boiler front. It has the front from the old 665, with a feedwater heater. The real Blue Comet had a feedwater heater. And although the Comet and Crescent are the same engine, the Comet runs better. The Crescent had trouble holding oil. Lionel added a small oil-light bearing to the brush plate of the Comet and it resulted in an improved performance.

Blue Comet bodies before being joined with motors.

8900 SANTA FE 4-6-4

1979. Unlike the Jersey Central's Blue Comet or the Southern's Crescent, neither of which were pulled by Hudsons, the Santa Fe did have a Hudson in its service. Lionel was accurate in that respect (although the real Santa Fe Hudson was a modified version of the one most familiar to Eastern railroads), but the tender was wrong. The engine and tender headed a new series called the "Famous American Railroad Series." There were freight cars with Santa Fe markings available for separate sale but the engine and tender came together, of course. The tender should have been the square-type used by the Santa Fe, rather than the rounded Pennsylvania-type.

"I know the square tender would have been more correct," says Bill Diss, "But the round tender is a little bigger and is established as our top tender, so we used it. There are a lot of different reasons why we do things and it is not always because we don't know any better. Sometimes we know it's wrong and we do it anyway."

The 8900 was the same engine as the 8603, but with Magne-Traction and spoked drivers.

Rejected 8900 steamers.

There are two big questions involving steamers that collectors most frequently ask: 1) Will Lionel make a Norfolk & Western Class J streamlined steamer? and 2) Will they make another 773-type Hudson? The answer to both questions would seem to be "probably." Lionel executives don't say what they are planning, but one gets the sense that both engines are in the works, with the Norfolk probably coming out before the Hudson. The tools to make the boilers for both engines are in good shape. The boiler tool for both engines have been tested and a photograph of the trial casting of the Norfolk is shown here. If, or when, the Hudson is made, it will be the postwar version and not the prewar scale or semi-scale versions.

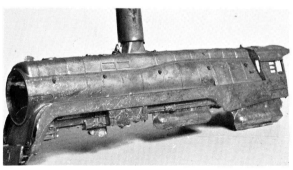

N&W trial casting.

That prewar 700E Hudson, incidentally, was used as a prototype model for a planned smoke unit back around 1945. A picture of it is shown, with the four zeros indicating it was a prototype, but not *the* prototype. The 700E in the photograph used the 0000 designation because the smoke unit is a prototype, not the engine. The prototype of the great 700E was made out of brass and was never painted.

The Hudson in the picture, which was on a shelf in Joe Bonnano's office for years, is a production model 700E which was modified to accept a handmake brass smoke unit, the bulb type that came out in 1946 on the 726 Berkshire and the 671 and 2020 steam turbines (See *Lionel: A Collectors Guide, Volume II* for details on postwar smoke units).

700E with prototype smoke unit. Shown in 46 catalog numbered 703.

But before either the Norfolk or the Hudson, there will come the remake of the old 736 Berkshire. That was scheduled for 1980. It will have the same motor that the original Berkshire had, a motor that Mount Clemens has never before produced. Since the old Norfolk & Western and the Berkshire used the same motor, the chances are the Norfolk will follow the Berkshire. At this stage of development it is probably harder to produce the motor mechanism than it is the casting. Once the mechanism is developed, the final steps in producing the Class J should be relatively easy.

Chessie Steam Special prototype.

The 1980 Berkshire was scheduled to be a model of a special Baltimore & Ohio excursion train that ran in 1977 and 1978 to celebrate its 150th birthday. The B&O prototype was an ex-Reading 4-8-4 that had been used as the American Freedom Train No. 1. It was repainted in the Chessie colors and ran across ten states, going on excursion runs for ticket buyers along the way. The color scheme was designed for the Chessie by Bob Lorenz, who designed the graphics for the Freedom Train, too.

"I first saw the Chessie Steam Special in the November 1978, issue of *Railfan* magazine," says Bill Diss. "I planned a Lionel version of the train to be done with the Blue Comet engine, but I changed to the Berkshire when we decided to do a Berkshire."

The Berkshire will have Magne-Traction and smoke and its tender will have six-wheel, die-cast trucks and Sound of Steam. It will also have a newly designed whistle that Lionel management expects will eliminate the problems of the first whistle.

The color scheme of the new engine is black with an orange and a yellow stripe, and the area around the boiler gray. A set of new-old passenger cars has been designed to go with the engine. They, like their prototypes, are yellow with orange stripes, blue trim, and a gray roof. The cars will be molded in blue plastic.

RATING

None of the big steamers is really scarce and none is as hard to find as the rare small steamers.
1. 8206 New York Central
2. 8600 New York Central
3. 8702 Southern

Chessie Steam Special with matching passenger cars.

SMALL

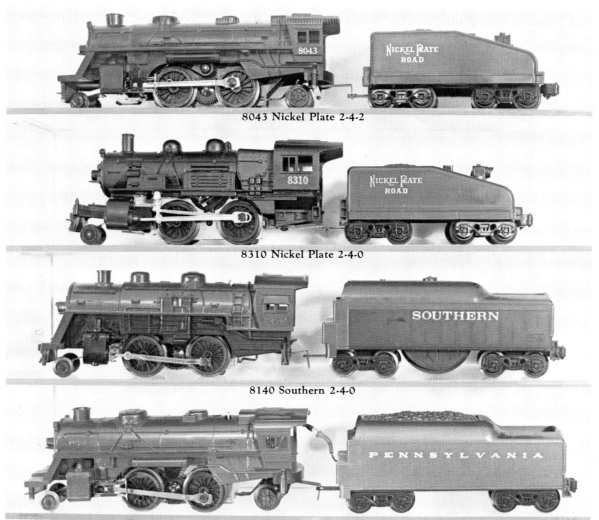

8043 Nickel Plate 2-4-2

8310 Nickel Plate 2-4-0

8140 Southern 2-4-0

8041 Pennsylvania 2-4-2

Most collectors ignore the small steamers in deference to the large ones. This is a mistake, because the most interesting and challenging of the steamers, from a collectors point of view, are the smaller ones. The top-of-the-line steamers are relatively easy to find, while some of the small ones are very difficult to find. The large steam engines vary little, but the small ones have some interesting variations. We cannot cover all the small steamers in this section, but we will cover the most interesting ones.

The small steamers came mostly in sets. They had a good motor, plastic or die-cast boilers and most had headlights. Some had electronic Sound of Steam, while others had the Sound of Steam simulated by means of BBs rolling about in a container under the tender. Some steamers had two-position reverse, while others had a manual reverse.

8140 SOUTHERN 2-4-0

There are two 8140s. One is black with a Nickel Plate tender, the other is a green Southern. The black was a Sears Special offered in 1971 and 1972. The green was available in 1973.

8040 CANADIAN NATIONAL 2-4-2

This engine was available in Canada only. It was shown in the 1972/1973 Canadian catalog heading a freight set.

8041 PENNSYLVANIA 2-4-2

The 8041 was originally shown in the 1970 catalog with no markings. It was available in 1971 but was not cataloged. It came with Sound of Steam and most collectors feel it was the test engine for that innovation. It is identical to the 8141 Pennsylvania 2-4-2 that came out in 1971. The 8141 was the first cataloged steamer to have the "Mighty Sound of Steam."

8043 NICKEL PLATE 2-4-2

1970. This was the first department store special set made by Lionel in Mount Clemens. It was sold through the Sears stores and was the same set, except for the engine, that was cataloged in 1970 and was headed by the common 8040 steamer. The 8043 did not come with smoke, or Sound of Steam.

8310 NICKEL PLATE 2-4-0

1973. This headed an uncataloged Sears special freight set. The engine came with three different tenders: 1) Slope-back tender with Nickel Plate markings, 2) Slope-back-type with Santa Fe markings, and 3) Pennsy-type coal with Jersey Central markings.

Two kinds of Jersey Central tenders exist. The more common is black plastic with gold lettering. The less common is painted black over blue plastic and is stamped with gold lettering.

8303 JERSEY CENTRAL

1974. The 8303 is not shown in the picture above. It is essentially the same engine as the 8041 Pennsylvania, except with an oil-style tender. But it is not the 8303 Jersey Central that Lionel produced that was particularly interesting; it is the 8303 that was not produced. As the picture below shows, the original plans for the 8303 were for it to be called the Blue Comet. A prototype was made.

"Everyone at Lionel was anxious to rape the Blue Comet name," says Dick Branstner. "Me included. Right off the bat we wanted to get a set out with 'Blue Comet' all over it. Lenny Dean talked us out of it."

Dean, always quality conscious, argued for patience.

"Wait until we can afford to make a really good steamer before we put the Blue Comet name on it," said Dean. "Make it the best."

Lionel waited. Collectors can be grateful to Dean it did.

RATING

All the small steamers mentioned in this section are rarer than any of the large steamers.
1. 8041 Pennsylvania
2. 8043 Nickel Plate
3. 8040 Canadian National

8303 Prototype.

Picture from 1980 Lionel catalogue.

SETS

The authors call the things on the opposite page "sets." Collectors call them sets. Dealers call them sets. Daddies call them sets, little boys call them sets and so do their sisters and their mothers and probably the family dogs, if you understand dog talk. But Lionel does not call the things on the opposite page sets.

Lionel calls them accessories.

Lionel has its own vocabulary and nomanclature about the things they sell. Lionel considers only engines and cars with track and transformers sets. Those sets are the mass market items Lionel sells to such places as K-Mart and Kiddie City. The cheaper bottom-of-the-line stuff. All the high quality items, the things collectors are interested in, are sold as individual pieces or as sets without the track or transformer. Lionel refers to those things officially as accessories.

Sometimes, of course, the individuals in the Lionel organization refer to the things on the opposite page as sets, just like everyone else, but that is not the official designation.

It is the belief of the higher-ups that its future rests in increasing the amount of sales to the mass market.

"Right now all sales are distributed about equally between sets and accessories, but we have to generate more sales out of sets, out of the mass market," says Jim Boosales. "We can't count on collectors forever as such a high percentage of our business."

Many collectors feel that Lionel should erase the distinction between the collecting market and the mass market and just make toy trains. Let collectible items arise from the mass market.

Now we will survey some of these things that dealers, dads and dogs call sets but that are really not sets at all.

ANNIVERSARY SET

There was a great deal of controversy among Lionel management about the 75th Anniversary Set. Not only was the disagreement about what the set should be — one proposal was to have a set that would display only the dif-

7506 "famous catalogs."

ferent Lionel logos through the years, rather than the gaudy graphics that were finally selected — but there was disagreement about *when* it should be. Some thought the anniversary should be 1978, based on the fact that the first Lionel catalog did not appear until 1903.

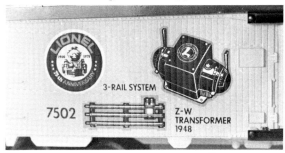

7502 depicting "innovations."

"I had to show them in the record book where it officially started in 1900," says Dick Branstner, engineering chief during the planning. Actually, says Branstner, the new General Mills management was not even thinking about an anniversary when Branstner first brought it up. "Nobody around there knew it was the 75th anniversary," he says.

COKE SET

The Coke set came about because they were popular drinks. "We thought a cola train would sell," says Bill Diss. "But it was a bummer. We had those things lying all over the place. I don't think we did the Coke set as well as we should have. The colors did not quite hit it. The Sprite car had sort of a weird green. The Coke company wasn't very concerned with how we did the cars. We just bought the cans from a local distributor and copied those. They did give us some color samples, but there is a difference putting the paint on aluminum and putting it on plastic. The aluminum gives the color a kind of candy apple effect that the plastic doesn't. The result is the colors are much brighter and vivid on the cans. Variations came about when we changed methods of applying graphics in an effort to get it perfect."

MICKEY MOUSE SET

The Mickey Mouse set had its origin in the decision by Lionel to make a hi-cube boxcar. There had been disagreement over how long to make the car when it first appeared in 1976. Bill Diss says he favored making the car the length of a passenger car. Dick Branstner says he favored making it two ways, boxcar length and passenger car length. Marketing Manager Sam Bushala decided to make it short.

"I felt there wasn't enough difference between that and our standard boxcars," says Diss. "We didn't have to go to the scale length but we could have made it longer so it would look different and we could have put more graphics on it. As it turned out the car was not well received. Because of the lack of response to the standard road names we went into the Mickey Mouse series with the car. We had the tooling and the car was not selling, so we decided to apply the car to a theme rather than to road names."

The Mickey Mouse set was an example of one of the rare times that Lionel paid a royalty for the use of a brand name.

"We went through licensing, approvals and lots of other things. Disney is very strict about how they want you to use their art. So we followed their art right to the letter. We had to make some modifications because of door stops and things like that, but basically we followed their directives."

One car that was added to the set after it first came out was the 9672 Mickey Mouse birthday boxcar. That was included in a year-end special to dealers (See U36B section) and was not cataloged. It is now the rarest car in the set. One dealer, Mike Diedling of Chicago, reported that when he received his year-end package, he got all the grosses of telephone poles and crossing signs and other things he did not particularly want, but the four Mickey Mouse cars had been carefully removed from the box. "It must have been an inside job at the factory," says Diedling. "Whoever did it cut out an area in the box where the cars had been and lifted them out. They knew exactly which part of the box to cut."

BICENTENNIAL SET

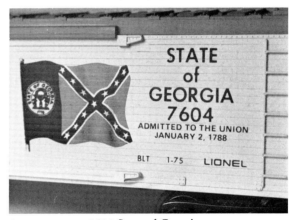

7604 State of Georgia.

The Bicentennial Set had 13 cars in it, for the original 13 colonies, of course, but the original plan called for many more cars than that.

"We were going to do all 50 states as they entered the union," says Diss. "We had all the research set up to do it that way. Then, after the first few cars were issued, sales tapered off and the idea was scratched. We dropped the state series and came out with other themes using the same cars."

GENERAL SET

The General Set is covered in detail in the STEAMER section.

BUDD CARS

An uncataloged service station set of Baltimore & Ohio Budd cars was released in 1977. The set contained three cars, the 8766 powered baggage, and the 8767 and 8768 dummy passengers. In late 1977 an 8764 powered passenger and 8765 dummy baggage were added to the set, both uncataloged. The following year a set of cataloged Amtrak Budd cars was offered. The set consisted of the 8868 powered baggage and three dummies: 8869 passenger, 8870 passenger and 8871 baggage.

The whole procedure of reissuing the Budd cars met with reserved approval on the part of dealers and the public. They liked the quality of both the B&O and Amtrak cars. Dealers reported that the service station set sold well, but not the two cars issued later in 1977.

"Maybe they should have brought out two dummies in 1978," says one dealer. "For the collector to get all five now, he has to spend a lot of money. I got stuck with the '78 cars. I think a lot of collectors missed them and they will turn out to be hard to find."

"We copied the way old Lionel did it," says Bill Diss. "They made a powered passenger and a powered baggage and we decided to make one passenger and one baggage powered."

The consensus is that Lionel did such a good job on the reissue of the B&O Budd cars that the price of the originals has gone down, as it has with the Virginian rectifier. The new Budd cars have the F-3 power and dummy trucks and, like the originals, have three-light illumination and operating couplers at both ends. Unlike the originals, there is neither horn nor Magne-Traction. The originals had a three-step pilot but the new ones have the same two-step pilot used on the geeps. The fuel tank is shorter than the one on the original and the B&O numerals are a darker shade of blue. The paint on the new cars has more metal flake, giving the surface a grainy look. On some units the Budd graphic is missing from the side.

The introduction of the Amtrak set met with a generally favorable response from collectors, who were happy to see something new. There is however, a feeling among some collectors that the Budd car has seen its day and that perhaps no more should be issued. The real Budd cars are almost as extinct as the steam engine, being used by only a few Eastern railroads. Those that are in use are dilapidated. But then, one of the charms of toy trains is that extinct items can live forever, glistening as if they had just rolled out of the shops.

The Budd cars were the first Service Station sets not to be freight sets. Service Station sets were first offered in 1971. They were limited edition sets that were offered exclusively to service station dealers.

"Service stations were squawking at that time that they weren't getting a fair shake," says Dick Branstner. "We talked to Lenny Dean, the service manager. He talked to a lot of the service centers about it. Their main complaint was that no matter what Lionel made you could buy it at any of the big chains cheaper than any of the service stations could possibly sell it. The service stations wanted a product line that only they could buy and sell. Lenny came up with the idea of a train set. It was a way of rewarding the service stations for all the repairs they had to do on trains that were bought somewhere else. We wanted to keep them interested in being a service station. It was successful, too."

But 1978 was the last year for the Service Station sets. It ended with the M & St. L GP-9 set.

"What was happening," say Fundimensions President James Boosales, "was that a lot of service stations that were also distributors would buy the service station sets in large quantities and resell them to dealers. This was not our intention. Those service stations that got most upset about discontinuing the sets were those that made money by cornering the market on them. Some service stations were not regular customers. They could just order parts. Some of them were actually phony. What we did was go through all our service stations and weeded out the phony ones. We now have 500 signed up under new criteria and we have some in every state in the country."

PASSENGER CARS

Almost from the beginning of the General Mills era, Lionel was urged by collectors to bring back the Irvington cars. What the collectors did not know was that the Irvington dies were no longer in existence, having been accidentally scrapped back in 1951 (see HISTORY). Lionel wanted to bring out a pre-streamlined style passenger car but discounted reviving the Irvington.

"We just weren't prepared to do a car like the Irvington from scratch," says former engineering director Dick Branstner. "I decided to do a compromise car. Come out with a nice-looking car based on the same kind of prototype the Irvington was based on."

Branstner sent a Canadian designer, Gordon Hathaway, to Toronto to take pictures of old passenger cars sitting around the Toronto yards. Hathaway took the dimensions of all the cars he photographed. He returned to Windsor and made wood mock-ups.

"We made a bunch of wood models of various lengths and widths and ran them with standard trucks to find out if they would clear all the accessories," says Branstner. "We did that a lot with any new item. If they didn't clear we would shape and narrow them until they did. The extremities of the wooden block were the same as the model we would eventually make. Sometimes we even took pictures of the wooden mock-up for the catalog. You can see the passenger car mock-ups in the advance catalog that came out in the spring of 1973."

MILWAUKEE SPECIAL
BROADWAY LIMITED
CAPITOL LIMITED

The first new old-style cars, as they are sometimes called, the Milwaukee Road "Milwaukee Special," came out in 1973. There were two Pullmans and an observation car in the set. The next year the Pennsylvania "Broadway Limited" appeared with the same consist. These cars were made with the same tool. Inserts were used in the tool in 1976 to change it so that it would make the combination car. The first all-baggage cars were also introduced in 1976 and they required a new tool, which cost $30,000.

The Baltimore & Ohio "Capitol Limited" set came out in 1975. Like the "Milwaukee Special" and the "Broadway Limited" before it, none of the cars in the B&O set were available for separate sale.

CAMPAIGN SPECIALS

For some reason, by the time 1976 approached, Lionel found itself stuck with a lot of unsold observation cars. Dan Johns, assistant to engineering vice-president Sam Bushala, then conceived of the idea to do the "campaign specials," three uncataloged observation cars offered in a spring flyer that had simulated bunting on the sides and an American flag hanging over the platform. On the rear platform of the 9527 Milwaukee Road there was a picture of President Roosevelt; on the 9528 Pennsylvania there was a picture of President Truman; and on the 9529 B&O there was a picture of President Eisenhower.

"Frankly, those campaign specials were just an election year gimmick to try to unload the surplus observation cars," admits one Lionel executive.

SOUTHERN CRESCENT

Probably the chief lobbyist for the Southern Crescent passenger cars, which came out in 1977, was Bill Diss of the engineering department. He pushed for the intricate decorating on both the Crescent and Blue Comet sets.

"It's a proven fact that an attractive passenger set will always sell," says Diss, who uses many reference books to check on various passenger trains of the past. The Southern Railroad was cooperative and the passenger cars have the authentic markings of the originals. "Whenever we wanted to do a Southern item their president, Graham Claytor, was a great help. I sent him both the F-3 and the Crescent with a note of thanks."

Southern Crescent
Pennsylvania RR
Pennsylvania RR aluminum cars
Milwaukee Road
Baltimore & Ohio

Passenger car mock-ups as shown in 1973 advance catalog.

BLUE COMET

Lionel had been talking about doing a Blue Comet set off and on since 1973. It was the success of the Crescent that made them decide to come out with the Blue Comet cars in 1978. "It was a natural," says Diss. "It is one of the great names in toy trains. We wanted this set to be the same as the original Lionel Standard gauge set, so we named the cars the same. When it was decided to add more cars besides the original three, we made sure the cars were named the same as cars that were in the real train."

Blue Comet passenger cars.

The three cars that were named the same as their Standard gauge ancestors were the 9538 Faye and 9539 Westphal passengers, and the 9540 Tempel observation. The 9536 Bernard baggage and 9537 Halley combination were names that did not appear in the original Lionel set.

Lionel's Blue Comet cars were the first to have six-wheel trucks, and they were die-cast metal instead of plastic. That the trucks were die-cast was intentional, that they were six-wheel was practically an accident. Fundimensions chief, Jim Boosales, tells that story:

"We were sitting around one day and I said, 'It's really silly that we didn't have metal trucks on the Southern Crescent. Can we get metal trucks? They said they didn't have enough capacity on their tool. I said, 'Build another tool. How much can a die-cast tool cost? It's not going to kill us.' I just figured they would copy the Southern Crescent four-wheel truck and make it metal. It's cheap. But somehow the die was made six-wheel. It ended up we had to change the tooling on every one of those cars for clearance, for tolerance, for hit points. It all cost about $70,000. But, of course, now we have a great six-wheel truck. And we can use it on other things."

The truck was added to top-of-the-line tenders for 1980.

TTOS CARS

The Toy Train Operating Society had Lionel make up a series of new old-style cars during the mid-1970s. The first was the 9512 Summerdale Junction Pullman, which was produced for the 1974 TTOS national convention. In 1975 the TTOS had a 9520 Phoenix, Arizona combination car made. In 1976 the car was a 9526 Snowbird, Utah observation. In 1977 the car was a 9535 Columbus, Ohio baggage. All the cars were yellow with maroon roofs. All, of course, were uncataloged. Those TTOS members who actually attended the conventions in the various cities received cars with special decals indicating they were there.

ALUMINUM CARS

Lionel came out with the aluminum passenger cars in 1979, in spite of the fact that Williams Manufacturing had been doing a very nice job of reproducing the original Lionel cars since 1975. In a way, Williams might have motivated Lionel because until then the project had been talked about for several years but not acted upon.

"My production people came to me after Lenny Dean had suggested making the cars to them," says Boosales. "They said, 'We can do these aluminum cars. We checked the tooling out, we've got it all, and we can do a better job than ever has been done.' I think they did."

Tuscan stripes being applied.

So do collectors. The new Lionel model is superior to the old in its finish and, as opposed to Williams, has operating couplers. The cars, in Pennsylvania markings, have Tuscan stripes, which are applied by hand on the assembly line.

The cars have the same names as their postwar Congressional set predecessors: 9571 William Penn passenger; 9572 Molly Pitcher passenger; 9573 Betsy Ross vista dome; and 9574 Alexander Hamilton observation. There is also a 9570 Railway Express baggage car without the side stripe.

The aluminum extrusions are made for Lionel by an outside vendor. Lionel adds the trucks, couplers, stripes and the illumination. Damaged extrusions, as the picture below shows, are, of course, returned to the vendor.

The vista dome itself is molded in clear plastic by Lionel. An elaborate paint mask, the most complicated one Lionel employs, is used to cover the window portion of the dome and paint the borders aluminum.

Vista Dome mask.

Before and after.

The new cars are treated in such a way that they can be painted, whereas the old cars did not take paint well. That has led Lionel management to seriously consider painting some cars, with possibilities for the future being a green set to go with the Crescent F-3, or a set in Daylight colors.

But the first thing planned for the aluminum cars was a group of five which would be available for separate sale in 1980. They would have Burlington markings, but not the plastic strips inserted along the sides. The cars were designed to comprise a Zephyr set along with a new Burlington F-3, which will be chromed but dulled to look like aluminum. The cars would be named after the cars in the old Denver Zephyr. There would be a baggage car, "The Silver Pouch;" a passenger car, "The Silver Halter;" two vista domes, "The Silver Kettle;" and "The Silver Gladiola;" and an observation, "The Silver Veranda."

"I first got the idea after seeing a color photograph from the Vanishing Vistas series of postcards," says Bill Diss. "It was a picture of the old Texas Zephyr. I thought it would be ideal for our F-3 and aluminum cars. We eventually used the names of the cars from the Colorado Zephyr. On the real train the names were stamped in black on a plate that was attached to the sides of the cars. We won't use a plate. The Burlington name and the car names will be rubber-stamped in black directly on the cars. The engine will have silver trucks and plans are for the cars to have silver, too."

Pete Sappenfield was quite enthusiastic about the new chrome look of the engine. "I've been a mother hen over the chroming of those engines and they will look as close as you can get to the original look of the aluminum prototype. The Burlington herald will be on the nose and 'Burlington' in block letters along the side."

Damaged extrusions.

RATING

The baggage cars for the Milwaukee Road, the Pennsylvania and the Baltimore & Ohio are the most sought-after of the cars in this section.

Burlington F-3 units.

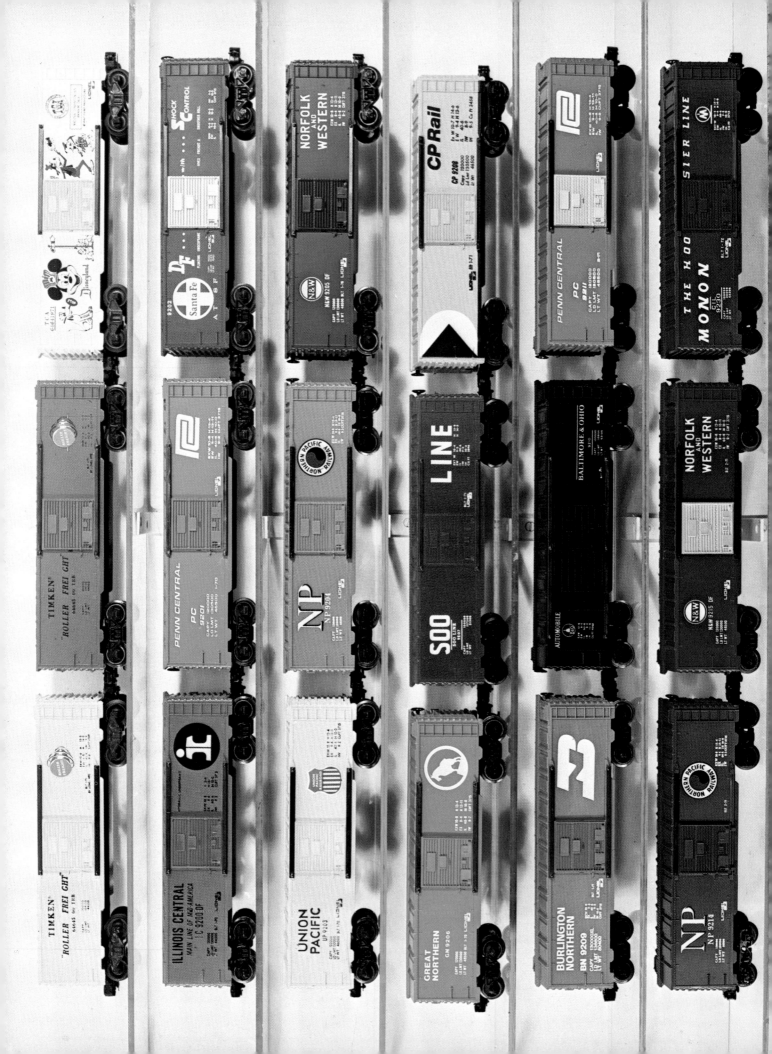

ROLLING STOCK
BOXCARS

When Mount Clemens announced their "Famous Name Boxcar Series" in the 1970 catalog, there was dancing at the meets. Had collectors known what they were getting into perhaps they would have sat that number out.

Through 1979, Lionel has made 65 different road names and lots of variations. They have also introduced marketing gimmicks that have made it very costly to be a boxcar collector.

One gimmick is Lionel's policy of including a collectable boxcar in a set only and not offering it for separate sale. This means the collector has to buy the entire set to get the one car. Some dealers break up the sets and sell the desirable cars separately but at a premium. Either way, it costs the collector extra money.

The most blatant example of exploiting the collector occured in 1978 and 1979 with the "Great Plains Express" set. In 1978 the set came with a CP Rail boxcar in black with white lettering numbered 9729. In 1979 the set was available again, but this time the CP Rail car had gold lettering and the number was changed to 9417.

Lionel expert John Palm comments: "First of all the set was way over-priced. The only decent car was the CP Rail box. I don't mind buying an entire set to get one car but they should at least include some other decent cars. To compound things they had the nerve to run the same set again but with the CP Rail car slightly changed. Not only does the collector get ripped the first time by having to buy the over-priced set, he has to buy the same set again to get the slightly-changed CP Rail car. If that isn't ripping off the collector I don't know what is."

Lionel's Bill Diss: "The change was requested by a large account in the East. Maybe they thought it was the only way the set would sell. It's easy for us to make a minor change like that. All we have to do is change the color of the tape on the hot-stamping machine. I certainly don't condone something like that. It creates ill-will."

President Jim Boosales: "We do not have a strategy to milk the collector. What happened with the Great Plains Set was a mistake. A bad idea. I assure you it will not happen again."

By late 1979 Lionel had in the works a series of five boxcars that would be released in 1980. The cars would commemorate the birth of Joshua Lionel Cowen, who was born on August 25, 1880. Each of these 100th birthday cars would represent an era of Lionel productivity and feature logos from that era. Lionel decided to offer only three cars for separate sale. The other two would be in Limited Edition sets, one in each set. To get all five cars, therefore, a collector would have to buy the three cars offered in open sale and two entire Limited Edition sets.

It was not known what Lionel called its marketing strategy for the Cowen birthday cars, but "Basic Collector Milking" would serve as a working title.

But there was evidence that Lionel, while not exactly conducting a fire sale on the JLC Birthday cars, had at least tried to make the other cars in the Limited Edition sets of decent quality, as John Palm had suggested. One set would be called the Royal Limited and would include a Chessie crane car with six-wheel trucks, a radioactive waste car, a Citgo triple-dome tanker, a Western Maryland reefer, and would be headed by a U36C in Chessie colors and Western Maryland markings, with silver trucks. It would have a matching caboose.

Royal Limited.

The other set containing a Cowen Birthday car would be called the Mid-Atlantic Limited. It would be headed by a new Seaboard SD-9 (a GP-9 with six-wheel trucks) with matching caboose and would include a 16-wheel depressed center flat car and four other cars.

"The two sets that will include the Joshua Lionel Cowen cars are made up of items that collectors will want anyway so we are not

forcing them to do something they don't want to do," says Bill Diss.

PROTOTYPE: JLC birthday car before historical data added.

Bill Diss had the idea of using the logos on the Cowen set. Diss had originally pushed to have a similar theme used on Lionel's 75th anniversary set, but lost out to Sam Bashala's idea of different products. The original plans for the birthday cars called for the boxcars to be issued in the 7800 tobacco series, but Diss, in late 1979, lobbied to have the cars be part of the 9400 series. His idea was accepted.

In 1978 Lionel changed the number of its Famous Name Boxcar series to 9400, but 9700 numbers still remain.

"There's enough 9700 numbers left to issue at least two 9700 cars for the next ten years," explains one boxcar collector. "The new Reading set has a 9700 car. So does the Southern Pacific set. I'm sure that's their plan: put 9700 boxcars in their top sets and force the boxcar collector to buy the whole set. It's really not such a bad idea if they make an effort to make the other cars in the set worthwhile. I understand their problems. I want them to keep making trains. I just hope they understand some of my problems, foremost of which is that I am not the Shah of Iran."

Actually, the boxcars are a good buy for around $14, considering inflation, the quality of the car, and what they charge for engines.

Some of the new boxcars produced by Lionel are very hard to acquire. In fact, the 9202 orange Santa Fe, made in 1970, is about as hard to find as any freight car ever produced by Lionel. In 1979 one changed hands at a meet in Florida for $650. Compare that price with the going price of an 813 rubber-stamped cattle car or a 6464-100 Western Pacific with the blue feather.

While essentially the 9200-9700-9400 boxcar that Lionel has been making in Michigan is the old 6464 car, there have been several improvements. The graphics are better than on the old cars and so are the paint jobs. The cars are molded in a color of plastic that is very close to the color the car will eventually be painted. This means that chips won't show. But perhaps the most important improvements in the cars are the tapered wheels and fixed, live axles.

The tapered wheel permits needle bearings in the tip of the axles, and these needle bearings, which lock into the truck frame, keep friction to an absolute minimum, since so little surface is rubbing against surface at the point of truck frame-axle contact. The only way it is possible to have the fixed, two-wheel axle is to have the wheels properly tapered so that they create differential action on curves, the outside (or smaller circumferenced) part of one wheel moving faster than the inside (or larger circumferenced) part of the other wheel. The way old Lionel created wheel differential on curves was to have each wheel connected to the truck frame by its own flat-end axle. The friction was so much greater that way that the same locomotive can pull five to six times as many cars under the new system.

There have been several changes common to all boxcars through the years. These were to the door guides, the end numberboards and the trucks.

The door guides: In 1970 and early 1971 double, metal door guides were used. In about mid-1971 Lionel experimented with double plastic door guides. They broke easily and in general were a bad idea. In late 1971 Lionel went back to the double metal door guides. In 1972 they went to a single, upper plastic door guide and have stayed with that type ever since. The single plastic door guide marked the beginning of the 9700 series. There are some boxcars whose numbers appear with all three types of door guides.

The end numberboards: In 1970 the end numberboards were blank. In 1971 one board said "Lionel/MPC" and the other said "9200 Series." In early 1972 some of the first 9700 cars appeared with "9200 Series" still on the numberboards. In mid-1972 the numberboard was changed to read "9700 Series."

The trucks: In 1970 leftover Timken-style trucks were used. In 1971 and after, Allied Full-Cushion trucks have been used.

Several of the characteristics of the boxcars in this section are common to other rolling stock as well. These characteristics include the improved graphics, painting and wheels and axles. And, like the boxcar, there are many types of collectors. Here are a few:

SERIES COLLECTORS. These people want every car in a series; for instance, all the 9700 cars. Lionel produced a number of uncataloged and special cars, some of which are numbered in the same series as the Famous Name series. Examples of these specials are cars made for collectors organizations, such as the Train Collectors Association and the Lionel Collector's Club of America. Other examples are promotional items like the Johnny Cash car and various cars made for the Toy Fair held in New York each January. Lionel also makes a car that is only available to customers who place large orders for slow-selling accessories like telephone poles (see U36 B section). All these cars are made in much lower quantities than the regular production cars. The predominant feeling among collectors, however, is that to have a complete series collection, such as the 9700 series, you have to have every car that starts with the 97 prefix, whether it be a TCA, Toy Fair, or cataloged car. For this reason we have included all types of special cars, both in the photographs and in the ratings.

REGULAR PRODUCTION COLLECTORS. They collect all the boxcars that appear in the regular catalog. They don't concern themselves with uncataloged cars, variations, mistakes or anything else. They just want one specimen of each car shown in the catalog. They are the least ambitious of all the boxcar collectors.

VARIATION COLLECTORS. They specialize in legitimate variations. By legitimate variations collectors mean something is changed during the production run or runs. Take the 9200 Illinois Central, for instance. It comes with the three different types of door guides and many more minor types of variations having to do with type of body mold, body color, mold color, door color, door mold color, size of letters, color of letters and positioning of letters. One observant collector reports having 12 distinctly different 9200 cars. This book will ignore all minor variations and comment only on major variations like the door guides. We do not want to offend sensitive variation collectors and trust they realize this book only has 144 pages.

MISTAKE COLLECTORS. Usually a mistake has to do with graphics. Examples of mistakes would be missing graphics, graphics applied upside down, at an angle, or twice (double-stamped).

All kinds of strange cars have turned up in the decade of the '70s, giving credence to the report that it used to be possible to go to the plant in Mount Clemens, slip a foreman some cash, and have crazy cars made up while you waited. Most collectors do not recognize mistakes as collectable pieces because they are, after all, mistakes and because they could have been created illigitimately. Among mistake buffs a highly prized car is the 9739 Denver & Rio Grande boxcar. The correct version has a stripe running along the side, separating the yellow and silver colors. The mistake car does not have the black line.

OVER-STAMP CAR COLLECTORS. Occasionally Lionel would pick a car from their inventory, usually a slow-seller, and make an additional stamping over the existing graphics. Examples are the Season's Greetings and Toy Fair cars. As in the case of the mistake cars, not all collectors are interested in the over-stamped cars.

In the boxcar section, as well as the other sections of rolling stock, not all cars that were made in the decade of the 1970s will be written about. It would be impossible to do so in a reasonable amount of space and many of the items are not important enough, from a collecting standpoint, to write about. Items examined in all the rolling stock sections will be limited to those that collectors feel are the most desirable, or have some other unique point of interest. Also eliminated from detailed consideration are cars made in such small quantities that they are virtually impossible to collect. An example would be the 9705 Rio Grande boxcar in silver. 21 of those were made as a color test.

As far as ratings, in most catagories of rolling stock, none has been established. All cars in a catagory frequently are equally available and not hard to find. Because so few cars in a single catagory of rolling stock may be rare, we have sometimes shown several different catagories in one color photograph. The resulting photographs may seem a bit hodge-podge at times, but space limitations would prevent showing large color photographs of only one or two items on a page.

9744 Tab

9748 CP Rail

9751 Frisco

9754 NYC

9758 Alaska

9743 Sprite

9747 C&O

9750 DT&I

9753 Maine Central

9757 Central of Georgia

9742 Minn. & St. L.

9745 Fanta

9749 Penn Central

9752 L&N

9755 UP

9764 Grand Trunk

9769 B&L&E

9772 GN

9775 Minn. & St. L

9778 Seasons Greetngs

9781 Delaware & Hudson

9763 Rio Grande

9768 Boston & Maine

9771 NW

9774 TCA

9777 Virginian

9780 Johnny Cash

9767 Rail Box

9770 NP

9773 NYC

9776 SP

9779 TCA

FAMOUS NAME COLLECTOR SERIES

9202 ORANGE SANTA FE

1970. The regular run of the 9202 Santa Fe was red with white lettering. It was the first boxcar to be made in Mount Clemens. But before the regular run of red 9202 was begun, about 130 orange ones came out of the molding machine. Some of them were stamped with black markings and how that all came about is an interesting story.

When an injection molding machine is fired-up for a run, it is common procedure to send about 150 shells, or shots, through for practice. This makes sure the machine is working properly, that there are no flash marks on the shots, and that the machine is purged of any plastic that is left over from the previous run. When the molding machine was fired-up for the 9202 Santa Fe, there was still some orange plastic left in it from the last time it had been used in Hillside, New Jersey. It took approximately 130 shots before the orange plastic was exhausted. Then the red plastic pellets were fed into the machine and the regular production run of the 9202 begun.

Normally the practice shots are discarded or recycled, but Lee Jones, who in 1970 was manager of manufacturing for Lionel, had an idea. He knew that Lionel had in the past made special cars for special occasions and, accurately concluding that the manufacture of the first boxcar in Mount Clemens was a special occasion, he salvaged some of the orange trial shots. His idea was to add trucks, trim, and lettering and give them to production line workers and others.

Of those 130 trial shots, 77 were in good enough condition to be made into finished cars. Jones took them over to the hot-stamping machines, which were set up with white tape for the red 9202. He changed the tape on one of the machines to black and started stamping his special car. Ten were ruined getting the hot-stamping machine to work properly, so 67 orange and black 9202 Santa Fe boxcars were

finally distributed among the Lionel employees. Jones composed a letter thanking everyone for working so hard to get Lionel going again and distributed it along with the orange car. One of those who received a car was Dick Branstner, the head of engineering, who had put in long, grueling days in preparing the 1970 line.

"After working with all those trains for about a year I was given this orange boxcar," Branstner recalls. "I was sick of looking at trains. Who needed the car? I gave it away to a collector from Michigan who felt bad because he didn't get one."

The car is now one of the most sought after freight car Lionel ever made.

6464-1971 TCA CONVENTION

1971. Made for the TCA National Convention held at Disneyland. Designed by collector Ward Kimball, a former Disney animation artist. Like all items with a Disney theme, this car is highly prized by collectors.

9727 TENNESSEE, ALABAMA & GEORGIA

1973. Made for the Lionel Collectors Club of America's national convention. The club was small in 1973 and probably not more than 1,000 were made.

9778 SEASON'S GREETINGS

1975. Most valued of the special cars (Toy Fair and Season's Greetings cars) because it is the only one with a 9700-series number stamped on the car.

9762 TOY FAIR

1975. Valued less than the 9778 because the 9700 number was not stamped on the car.

9739 RIO GRANDE

1975. Came in the Rio Grande service station set in two versions. The common version has a black line separating the yellow and the silver. About 100 were made without the black line.

9701 BLACK BALTIMORE & OHIO

1971. Double-door automobile car. Common version is silver. About 1200 were painted black. Some of these black 9701's were given to the TCA to be used as door-prizes for their 1971 convention. The rest were purchased by the LCCA and used as their first national convention car. A decal was added to the cars sold to the LCCA.

6464-1970 TCA NATIONAL CONVENTION

1970. First collectors club car made by Mount Clemens and one of the first boxcars of any markings to be made there.

6464-500 TIMKEN

1970. Made at the request of long-time Lionel dealer Glen Uhl of Akron, Ohio. There are three versions: yellow with blank number-boards, orange with blank numberboards, and orange with 9200 on the numberboards.

"I asked about making the car because the Timken Company is in Canton, Ohio, near Akron," says Uhl. "Lionel had some Timken decals left over from New Jersey so I ordered as many cars as they had decals for. The final figure was just over 1,800. The original Lionel car was yellow with a white stripe. The real Timken car was orange. So we had both yellow and orange cars made. There were 500 yellow and 1,300 orange. Lionel did not want to put the white stripe on, so both the orange and the yellow cars are plain. The last 50 came with the 9200 numberboards."

Glen Uhl at a General Mills stockholder's meeting.

Glen Uhl is one of the most colorful figures in the toy train hobby. He's a familiar sight at train meets, often wearing an engineer's hat and overalls covered with railroad patches. He's been a big-volume Lionel dealer since 1945 and he is a direct-talking, no-nonsense businessman whose word is as good as a signed contract. Never hesitant to make his opinions known to Lionel big shots, he owns stock in the Lionel Corporation and during the turbulent days of the early 1960s, when the company was being run by Roy Cohn, Uhl attended the annual stockholders meetings in New York City, dressed in his railroad outfit, and could be counted on to stand up and give Cohn and the other members of the board of directors an earful on the sorry state of their organization.

Now in his 70s, Uhl has become no less verbose. He also owns stock in General Mills When the first GG-1s came out in 1977 and it was discovered they leaked grease, Uhl complained to Fundimensions President Jim Boosales.

"We went up to Lionel and saw Jim Finley, vice-president of production," says Uhl. "He showed me a plastic diaper they had developed which could be attached to the bottom of the red GG-1 (the 8753 Pennsylvania) and said they would send them to me. It was suppose to stop the leak. He said the same diaper would be put on the new black GG-1 (the 8850 Penn Central). But they didn't do it.

"When I got my shipment of black GG-1s they didn't have diapers. I called Lionel and told them I wanted to return all my GG-1s. Ninety-three of them. They said I couldn't do it because they don't take back merchandise. I said yes you will because I'm going to drop them up on your doorstep because I'm not going to pay for them."

Lionel knew by this time that Glen Uhl was a man of his word. He had already sent the executives at both General Mills and Lionel empty boxes of disposable diapers to show he had never received his promised plastic one. Lionel sent a truck and not only picked up the 93 GG-1s, they picked up all of Uhl's Lionel products.

"Ninety four thousand dollars worth of Lionel trains," says Uhl. "I didn't mind because I got rid of a lot of stuff like telephone poles I could never sell and got credit for them. Now I buy through a distributor. They closed my account and sent me a letter saying I would have to take down my sign that said 'Authorized Lionel Service Station.' So I put 'Un' in front of the 'Authorized' and sent a photograph of the sign to Boosales. Now I'm an 'Unauthorized Lionel Service Station.'"

And a year later Glen Uhl, not a man to be ignored whether he's authorized or unauthorized, sent another empty box of Pampers to Jim Finley.

9403 SEABOARD COASTLINE

1978. Common version is black with yellow lettering. A few were made with white lettering. Most of the cars with white lettering have turned up on the East Coast.

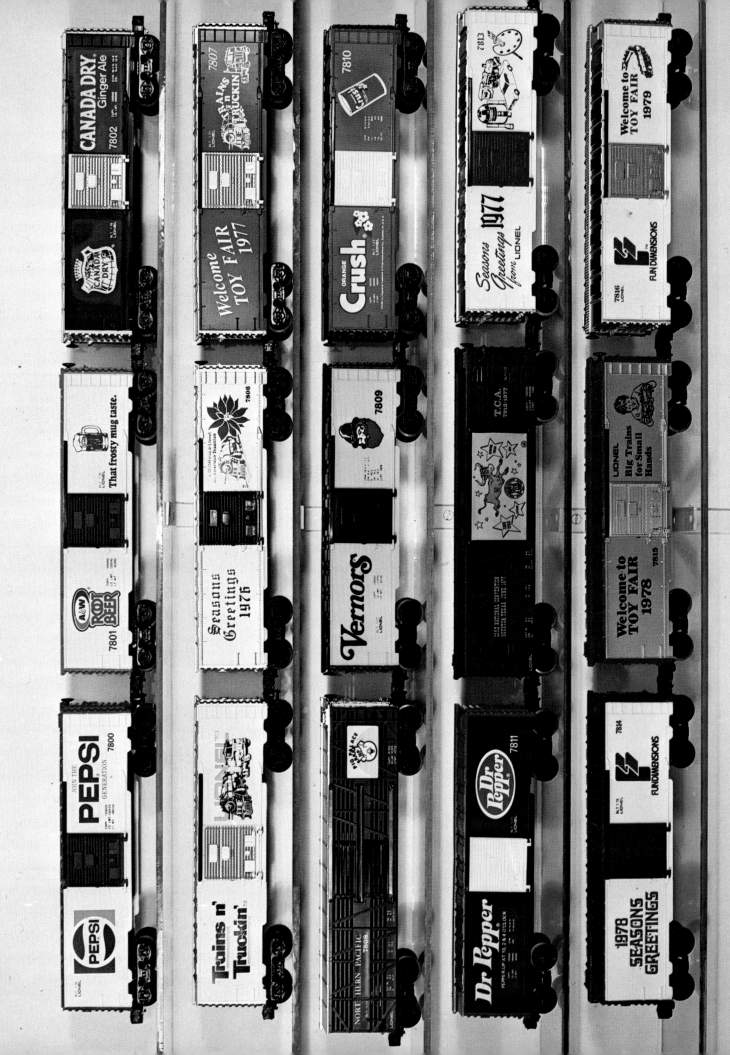

9703 CANADIAN PACIFIC

1972. Most sought-after of all the boxcars with the Canadian Pacific roadname.

9724 MISSOURI PACIFIC

1973. Came in Canadian Pacific service station set and later cataloged. One of the most handsome of the 9700 cars.

7700 SERIES

This series, with a newly styled boxcar, was introduced in 1976. The car, a little longer than the Famous Name boxcars, had simulated wood sides. It was used in the Spirit of '76 state car series, the Tobacco Railroad series, and as a special car. The car through 1979 had been assigned to only one real road name, the 7712 Santa Fe, released in 1979.

7705 CANADIAN TOY FAIR

1976. The only Toy Fair car to be made exclusively for the Canadian market, it is the most sought after of all the special cars. There were probably about 100 of them made and it is about the best looking of the Toy Fair cars.

7704 TOY FAIR

1976. Also one of the better looking of the Toy Fair cars.

7700 UNCLE SAM

1976. The car came in the Year-end Special package offered to dealers. For more about the Year-end Specials see page 69.

7800 SERIES

The 7800 series used the same mold as the Famous Name boxcars. It was introduced in 1977 and has been used for the pop cars series and several special cars. The cars listed in the following paragraph are the most sought-after of the 7800 series and all of them are about equal in availability. All other 7800 cars are also equal in availability, although easier to find than the cars listed.

7803 Trains 'N Truckin' (1978); 7806 Season's Greeting (1976); 7807 Toy Fair (1977); 7813 Season's Greetings (1977); 7814 Season's Greetings (1978); 7815 Toy Fair (1978); 7816 Toy Fair (1979); 7808 Northern Pacific, which came in the Heartland Express set only in 1977.

HI-CUBE BOXCARS

9605 New Haven.

Introduced in 1976, they never sold well. To re-coop the cost of the dies, Lionel decided to give the cars a Disney theme, thus assuring sales. All hi-cube boxcars except the Disneys are readily available and inexpensive. The Disney set is covered in SETS. Besides the Disney cars the 9605 New Haven is harder to find than the others.

027 BOXCARS

These smaller boxcars, which were 7-inches long, were introduced in 1970. They came in the lower-priced sets only. They had no sliding doors and non-operating couplers.

9090 GENERAL MILLS

1971. This car only had four wheels. The entire side of the car lifted up. It came in a set, the Yardmaster, and was available separately.

9045 TOYS R US

1975. This was the first promotional car made in Mount Clemens. It is the hardest to find of all the Toys R Us cars. It was un-cataloged.

9054 J. C. PENNEY

1977. This car was in the Trains 'N Truckin' set sold to J. C. Penney. It was painted gold to commemorate Penney's 50th anniversary.

MAJOR LEAGUE CARS

Scheduled for 1980 was a series of 9400 cars that would have the logos of major league sports teams. Two cars would have baseball names, two basketball and two hockey. There would be no football car because Lionel could not get permission from the National Football League to use the logos, even though Lionel paid royalties on this particular series.

"Football wouldn't play ball," quipped Pete Sappenfield. "The agent who handles giving out licenses for the NFL bowed out at the last minute. I guess they felt that trains weren't the thing for football. Royalties are the name of the game with them and they want a certain minimum number of units produced. I thought we met their numbers."

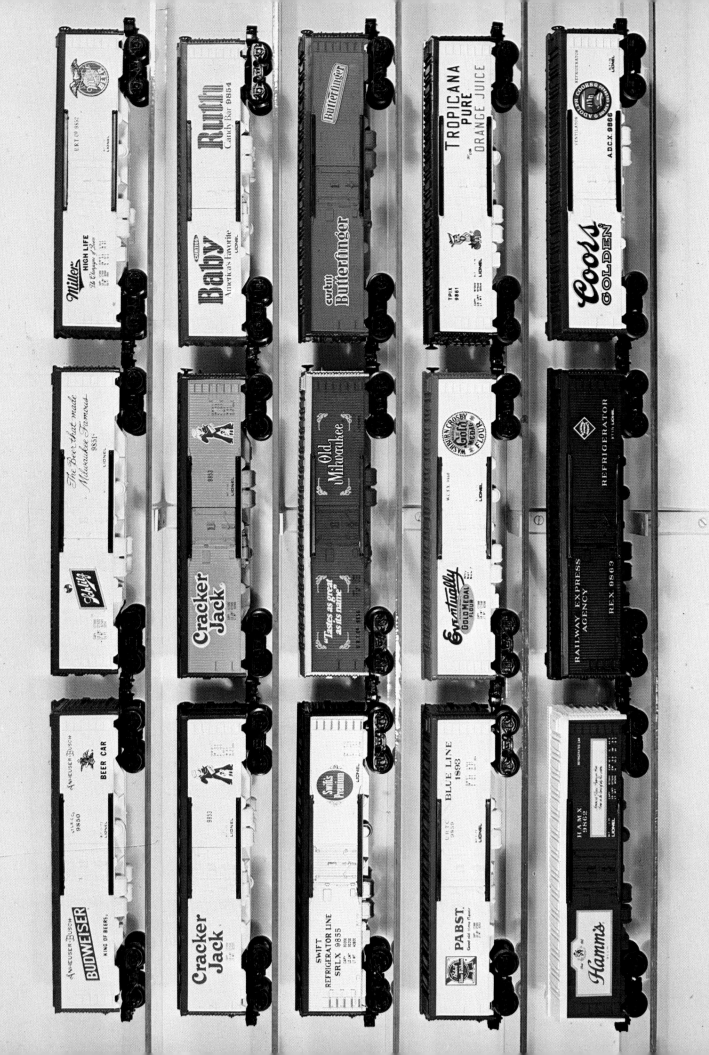

OTHER ROLLING STOCK
9800 BILLBOARD
REEFER SERIES

Introduced in 1973, the cars of the 9800 series featured excellent detailing and graphics. The cars were over 11 inches long and used the same tool the old Lionel had used on its 6572 Railway Express reefer in 1958 and 1959. The tool was modified slightly by adding simulated wooden slats. The original reefer was a smooth-sided car with rivets. On some of the early billboard cars there are still rivet marks on the sides, but you have to look closely to see them.

The reefer made some changes during the years. Metal door guides were used through 1975 but replaced by plastic in 1976. Also in 1976 the metal support strip under the floor was eliminated, the service doors were removed from the sides of the car next to the bottom of the ladder, and the ice hatch was removed from the roof.

Service doors.   Service doors removed.

The 9800 series has become quite popular but it almost did not come about. Management, except for Dick Branstner, resisted at first. "They felt the decorating would be too involved and expensive and that nobody would want a bunch of moving billboards," say Branstner. "I had a heck of a time selling them."

9853 CRACKER JACK

1973 through 1975. One of the original six billboard reefers introduced, the Cracker Jack car was cataloged with a caramel-colored body, darker brown roof, and red lettering. But most of the early cars off the assembly line had white bodies; then Lionel changed the bodies to caramel; finally they were switched back to white. The whole situation has become confusing for collectors, who want to know which came first, the caramel or the white, and why the switching back and forth? Here is the story:

The Cracker Jack car was pictured in the catalog with a white border surrounding the red "Cracker Jack" lettering. That's the way Lionel ordered the electrocal tape made. But the graphics sent to Lionel from the electrocal vendor did not have the white border around the lettering. The production run was begun with the borderless red lettering on the caramel-colored cars. Then Dick Branstner saw the cars.

"I thought it looked dumb without the white outline on the red lettering, so I switched the cars to white," says Branstner. "The lettering stood out much better. Then the electrocal outfit corrected their mistake and started sending us electrocal tapes with the correct white outline around the red lettering. So I switched back to the caramel-colored body."

That set off reverberations in collecting circles.

"We received all kinds of complaints from guys saying we purposely made a collectors item out of the white car. So I decided to remake the white car in order to even things out. By the time we quit making the cars, I think the caramel and white cars had been made in equal numbers."

A car harder to find than the others did emerge from all of this, of course: that original caramel-colored car with the red lettering without white border, the car Branstner ordered stopped. It is the most valuable item in the 9800 series.

Mirror shot of "Cracker Jack — Miller High Life" car.

The Cracker Jack car that was pictured in the 1973 catalog was hand-painted with the Cracker Jack markings on one side and with the 9852 Miller High Life markings on the

other. There was a rush to get the cars done before the picture deadline for the catalog passed. Both cars have the same color roof and to save time they just decorated one rather than two and flip-flopped it for the picture-taking session.

9863 RAILWAY EXPRESS

1975 and 1976. The Railway Express car is one of two reefers that covers the period when Lionel was switching from metal to plastic door guides and floor support strips. The early cars had metal, the later plastic. The Railway Express car with the plastic guides is more desirable than the one with metal.

The 9863 is also in demand because operators like to use it with their passenger sets.

9861 TROPICANA

1975 through 1977. This is the other billboard reefer that has both metal and plastic door guides and support strips, the change taking place in 1976. The 9861 with the metal support and guides is more sought-after than the plastic version.

KRAFT CAR

Kraft reefer prototype.

The Kraft billboard reefer was prominently displayed in the 1979 corporate catalog. That was a catalog that was actually three catalogs in one — the Lionel, MPC and Craft-Master catalogs all put together under one Fundimensions cover and distributed at the Toy Fair and other shows. But the Kraft reefer was never made. When the Lionel line came out the 9879 Kraft number appeared on the Hills Brothers Coffee reefer.

"What happened there," says former assistant products manager John Brady, "was that I contacted Kraft about using their name. We sent them a form letter similar to the one we send to the railroads, asking for any help in the selection of graphics. In the meantime I went out an bought a package of Kraft Philadelphia cream cheese. Bill Diss and I sat down with Dave Diehm, the head of the art department, and discussed what the colors should be and what the placement of the graphics on the car should be. He sketched a design and turned it over to Ron Rae, who did the actual art on the mylar.

"In the meantime we had a car painted in dark purple and silver. Then we sent the final art to Kraft and they okayed it by phone. We had the rubdowns made (rubdowns are what the Lionel people call dry transfers) and the mock-up was finished. Then we had it photographed and key-lined into the catalog, which went to press. A few days later we got a letter from Kraft saying their corporate policy was not to get involved in these kinds of things. It was a flat no, so we let it drop."

Almost all companies are glad to let Lionel use their names on items so that when a company refuses, as Kraft did, the Lionel management hardly gives it a thought. There are so many good graphics to choose from and so many companies willing to cooperate that Lionel quickly makes another selection. When the Kraft people said no, Bill Diss reassigned the Kraft car number to Hills Brothers.

Back to the drawing board.

What was unusual about the Kraft car situation was that the art was verbally approved by Kraft and the car then appeared in the catalog. Usually if a company is going to deny permission to use its name, it does so immediately and the project does not get as far as the Kraft reefer did. Tootsie Roll in 1978 refused permission for its name to be used on a tank car and Lionel made the Life Saver car only. The next year Tootsie Roll changed its mind and in 1979 the Tootsie Roll tanker appeared.

The Tootsie Roll tanker, which was numbered 9324, first appeared, like the Kraft car, in the 1979 Fundimensions corporate catalog,

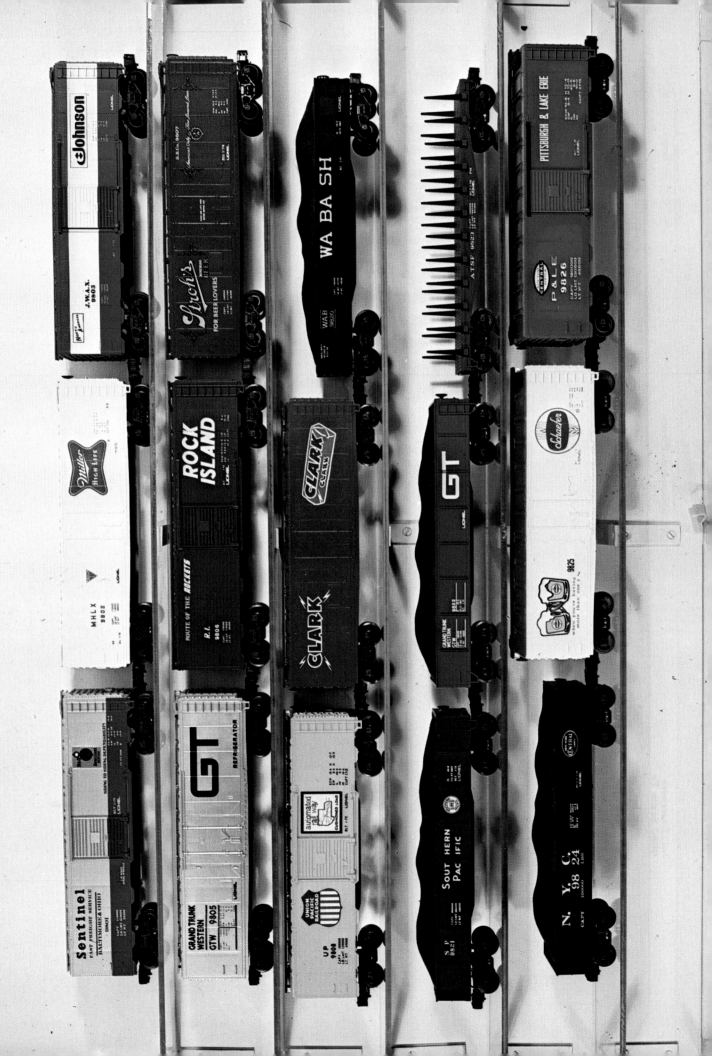

9803 Johnson's Wax
9807 Stroh's
9820 Wabash
9823 Santa Fe
9826 NYC

9802 Millers
9806 Rock Island
9809 Clark
9822 GTW
9825 Schaefer

9801 Sentinel
9805 GTW
9808 UP
9821 SP
9824 NYC

which was also called the "full line Toy Fair catalog" by the Fundimensions people. That catalog itself has become the subject of some misconceptions. For one reason or another, the Fundimensions companies, including Lionel, were not happy with the arrangements, and it is likely that in the future the three Fundimensions lines will keep their catalogs separate. Word has circulated that the 1979 corporate catalog is an extremely rare collectors item because only a few of them were made. One report said fewer than 1,000 were printed, and many of those were destroyed. The report is wrong.

"I don't know what the figure is based on," says Lionel Marketing Manager Pete Sappenfield, "but between 30,000 and 35,000 full line Toy Fair catalogs were printed. None of them have been destroyed." Sappenfield added that there were about 200,000 regular Lionel catalogs printed in 1979.

STANDARD O SERIES

Pola of Germany, a well-known European toy train maker, offered a complete line of scale cars to Lionel in 1972. George Toteff, who was president of MPC at the time, was interested and told Pola to send over a few samples. After seeing the samples Toteff offered Pola $20,000 for the molds, rather than buy the finished cars. Pola accepted the offer and in 1973 the first Standard O cars came out.

They were never too well-received, although they were well-made. They had nice detailing and sprung die-cast trucks. They were of a different proportion than other Lionel rolling stock and that could be the reason they were not big sellers. The first year Lionel brought out a reefer, boxcar, and gondola in two road names each. They added another road name to each car in 1974 and again in 1975, also adding a flatcar to the line in '75. They were still trying to get rid of the cars in 1976. Lionel had the dies to make a tank car and a caboose but they never did, dropping the line after 1976. Of the cars that were brought out, the gondola seemed to attract the least attention. But now that car is a hot item. In fact, the whole series is quite hot on the collectors market.

"All it takes is for Lionel to discontinue a series and everyone frantically tries to put a complete series together," according to Lionel dealer Mike Diedling. "I thought I would be stuck with those leftover Standard O cars, but now I wish I had more. If Lionel ever makes the tanker and caboose I think they would be good sellers."

No variations have been reported in the Standard O series, which would indicate that only one run was made of each road name.

RATING

1. 9808 Union Pacific boxcar
2. 9823 Santa Fe flatcar
3. 9806 Rock Island boxcar.

GONDOLAS

Mount Clemens was starting, by the 1980s, to pay more attention to gondolas, which had been generally ignored over the years. Some of the gondolas released by Lionel in the late 1970s had sprightly graphics and more were planned for the future.

9142 REPUBLIC STEEL

1971. Common in green with white lettering. Rare in Tuscan with yellow lettering.

9141 BURLINGTON NORTHERN

1971. Common in green. Rare in Tuscan. Rumor is that Lionel had leftover Tuscan bodies and they were stamped 9141 Burlington Northern.

9143 CANADIAN NATIONAL

1971 and 1972. Made for Canadian market. Not many show up in the United States.

VAT CARS

There were three vat cars made in the first 10 years of the new Lionel.

9128 HEINZ PICKLE CAR

1974 through 1976. The vats on the Heinz car came in three different shades of yellow. The lettering on the vats came in different colors, and sometimes there was no lettering.

9132 LIBBY PINEAPPLE

1975 through 1977. No variations.

9146 MOGEN DAVID

1977. The vats on the Mogen David car also had a variation. Some were tan and some brown. It has not yet been determined which color vats is harder to find, if either one is.

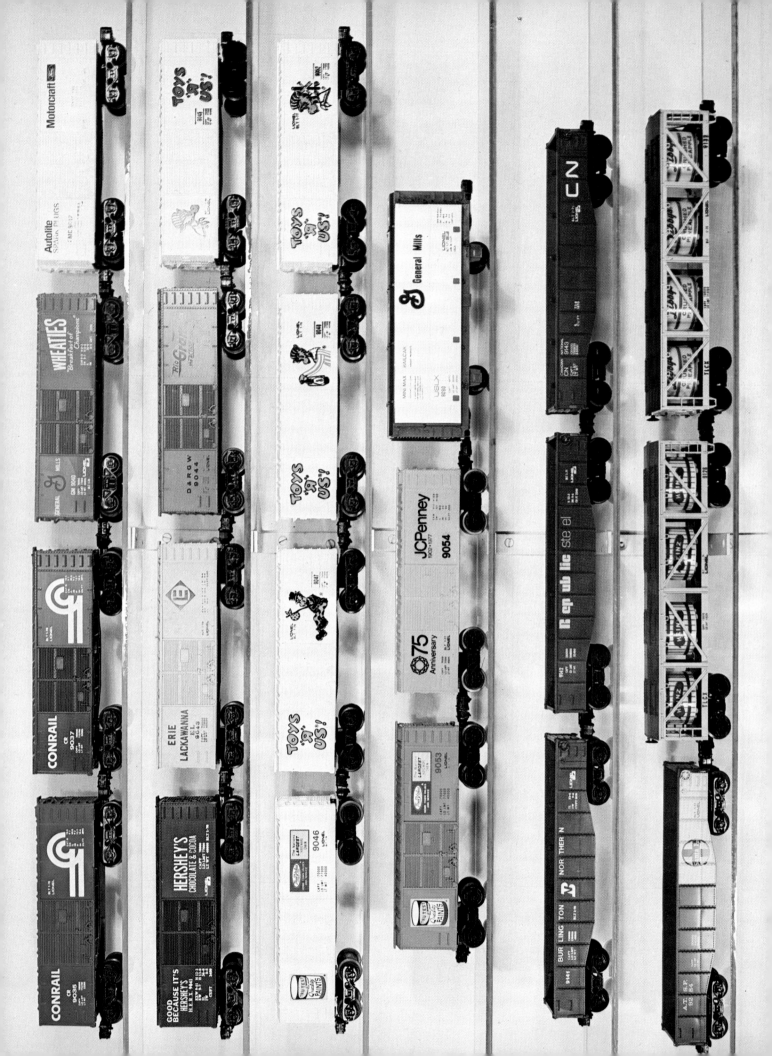

9250 Waterpoxy
9155 Monsanto
9273 Lifesavers

9151 Shell
9152 Shell
9324 Tootsie Roll

TANK CARS

Mount Clemens made three kinds of tank cars: single, single with platform, and triple dome.

Some of the early 9250 GMCX tankers came with leftover metal trucks and brakewheels. Later runs had plastic trucks and brakewheels. Of the regular run tankers only two could be considered hard-to-find: the 9150 Gulf made in 1971 and the 9151 Shell made in 1972.

Hand application of Life Saver decal.

Two cars made for collector associations are also sought-after: 9155 Monsanto, 1975 LCCA convention car, and the 6315, the convention car for the TCA in 1972.

HOPPERS

Mount Clemens made two hoppers, a small twin-bin type and a larger, covered hopper type. The small hoppers usually came in the low-priced sets. The large hoppers came in the better sets and were offered for separate sale, too.

Riveting trucks to DT&I hopper.

6446-25 NORFOLK & WESTERN
1970. Blue. Some collectors believe that car was run to test the mold.

9110 BALTIMORE & OHIO
1971 and 1972. Common versions have white or gray lettering. Rare version has yellow lettering.

9011 GREAT NORTHERN
1971. Common in powder blue. A dark blue version is rare.

9012 TA&G
1972. Common in dark blue. Rare version is medium blue.

9034 HAPPY HOPPER
1977. Uncataloged. Issued through Kiddy City chain, which is owned by the Lionel Corporation of New York, New York.

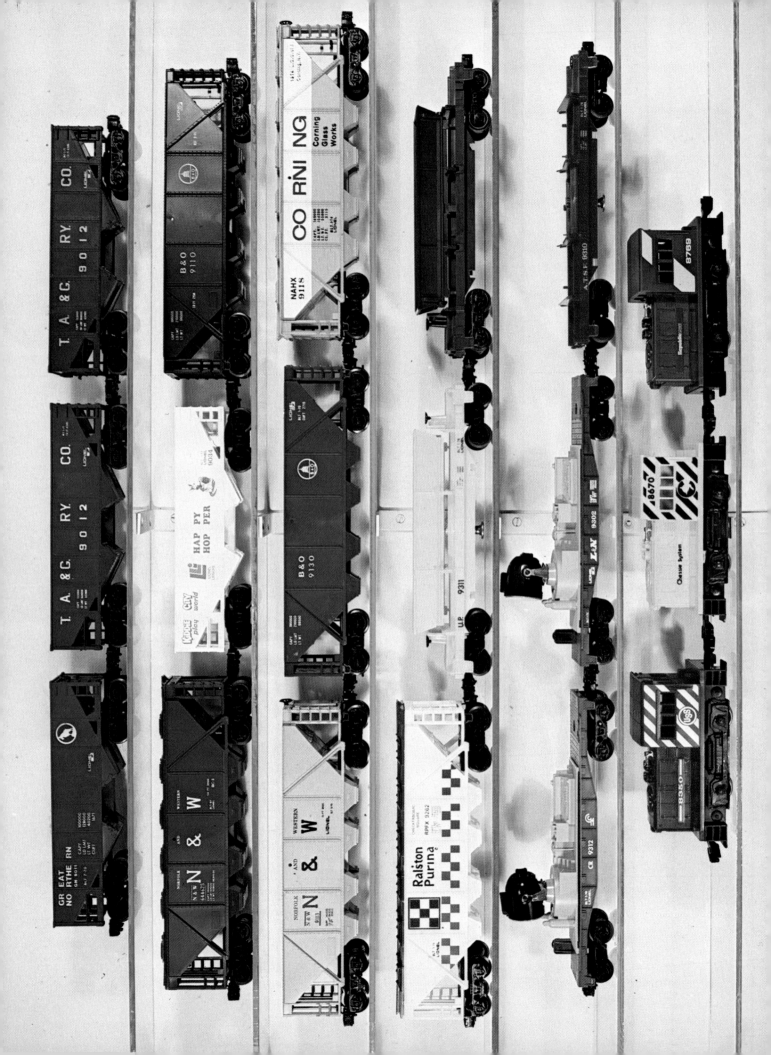

OPERATING CARS

The operating cars made by Lionel in the 1970s were an uninteresting group. About the only car worth mentioning is the 9302 Louisville & Nashville searchlight car with white lettering. Most have yellow lettering. A dump car with no lettering is shown.

FLAT CARS

9121 LOUISVILLE & NASHVILLE

1976. Common in brown with white lettering. Rare in red with yellow lettering.

9122 NORTHERN PACIFIC

Brown is the common color. Green is not common.

9020 UNION PACIFIC

1970. Available only in the Grand Trunk & Western set. It came in two colors, red and brown.

9023 MKT

1973 and 1974. Available only in the Rock Island Express set.

CRANE CARS

Prototype Chessie 12-wheel crane with passenger car couplers. Production car has coupler with shorter arm.

There has been some question whether or not the 6560 crane car was ever made by General Mills. It was. The car is shown with an MPC carton on page 122. The first crane car with all-new graphics to be put out by General Mills did not appear until 1979. It was green and yellow with Reading markings and was numbered 9332. It came in the Quaker City Limited set.

The first crane car to have die-cast, six-wheel trucks was scheduled to be released by Lionel in the spring of 1980. It would have Chessie markings and come in a set. There would also be a Santa Fe crane, but that would have four-wheel trucks.

AUTO CARRIERS

Lionel made two types of auto carriers: two-tier and three-tier. The two-tier version came in sets only while the three-tier were available for separate sale.

9123 TCA

1973 Train Collectors Association's national convention car. The regular production 9123 has Chesapeake & Ohio markings. The one shown in the photograph on page 122 is a good example of a mistake car. The C&O logo is stamped twice. It should be stamped only once. Three-tier.

9125 NORFOLK & WESTERN

1977. Common version is blue but some were molded black. Came in the Chesapeake Flyer set. Two-tier.

9123 CHESAPEAKE & OHIO

1974. Common versions are blue or black with the C&O herald stamped in yellow on the top tier of the two-tier car. The harder-to-find version has the logo stamped on both the top and bottom tiers.

9230 GOLD BULLION CAR

Gold Reserve car before painting.

1979. This car came with a Limited Edition set, the Southern Pacific Limited, which was headed by the new 8960 Southern Pacific U36C. The car was painted silver over a clear plastic shell. The bullions inside were painted gold. The number 9230 was heat-stamped in black on the side, as were the words "Fort Knox Gold Reserve" under the windows.

There is nothing, at this early date, that is particularly unusual about the 9230, except that some of the unpainted shells were stolen from the Lionel factory. These shells are perfectly clear plastic with the gold bricks inside. There are no numbers or letters on the shells; they were not heat-stamped on until the car was painted.

CABOOSES

Lionel made five different types of cabooses during its first decade in Mount Clemens. Except for the low-priced bobber, all the cabooses were the same as those offered by Lionel in the postwar period, 1946-1969.

PORTHOLE

The porthole, or round-window, caboose was a model of that used by the Pennsylvania Railroad. Although in actual practice the Pennsy was the only railroad to have the porthole caboose, Lionel has put many different road names on it. Among the more difficult to find of the porthole cabooses are the following:

9170 Norfolk & Western, which was cataloged in 1975.

9176 Bangor & Aroostock, which came with the Jerimiah O'Brien set in 1975 and was uncataloged. 1975.

9165 Canadian Pacific in Tuscan, which was uncataloged and came in the Canadian Pacific Service station special in 1973.

9160 Illinois Central, 1970 through 1972, the first porthole caboose. The first few made had the good postwar pick-ups and couplers at each end.

SOUTHERN PACIFIC-TYPE

The Southern Pacific-type caboose presents the biggest challenge for collectors because there are many odd color schemes and markings within it. Most of the SP cabooses came in sets and were not sold separately. Most were not illuminated.

The SP-style cabooses were for the most part bought by people other than collectors and many of them were worn out by kids playing with them. The collectors ignored them in the early days and although they pay more attention to them now, there is still not a great demand for them and although some of them are fairly scarce they still can be bought at reasonable prices. Here are some of the more interesting ones:

9060 Nickel Plate, 1970, with a Tuscan body. It is rare with a Tuscan frame and common with a black frame. It is the only caboose made with a frame that matches the cab.

9065 Canadian National in Tuscan was sold in Canada only in 1971 and 1972.

9063 Grand Trunk. It is hard to find in orange, but common in Tuscan. Made in 1970.

9070 Rock Island in gray, came in a Rock Island cataloged set in 1973 and 1974.

9075 Rock Island, came in uncataloged Sears set in 1975.

WORK CABOOSE

The original Lionel work caboose had a metal base that was only used on cabooses. Tabs secured the cab and tray to the frame. The new caboose uses a flat car with prongs that hold the cab and tray. The prongs break easily. An interesting one:

9021 Santa Fe was made 1970 through 1974 and its common color is red, but there is a hard-to-find orange.

BOBBER

This is the only new caboose to come out of Mount Clemens. The bobbers were sold in cheap sets and are ignored by most collectors.

9067 Kickapoo Valley came out in 1972 in a set only. It was issued in three colors: red, green and yellow. All came with gold trim.

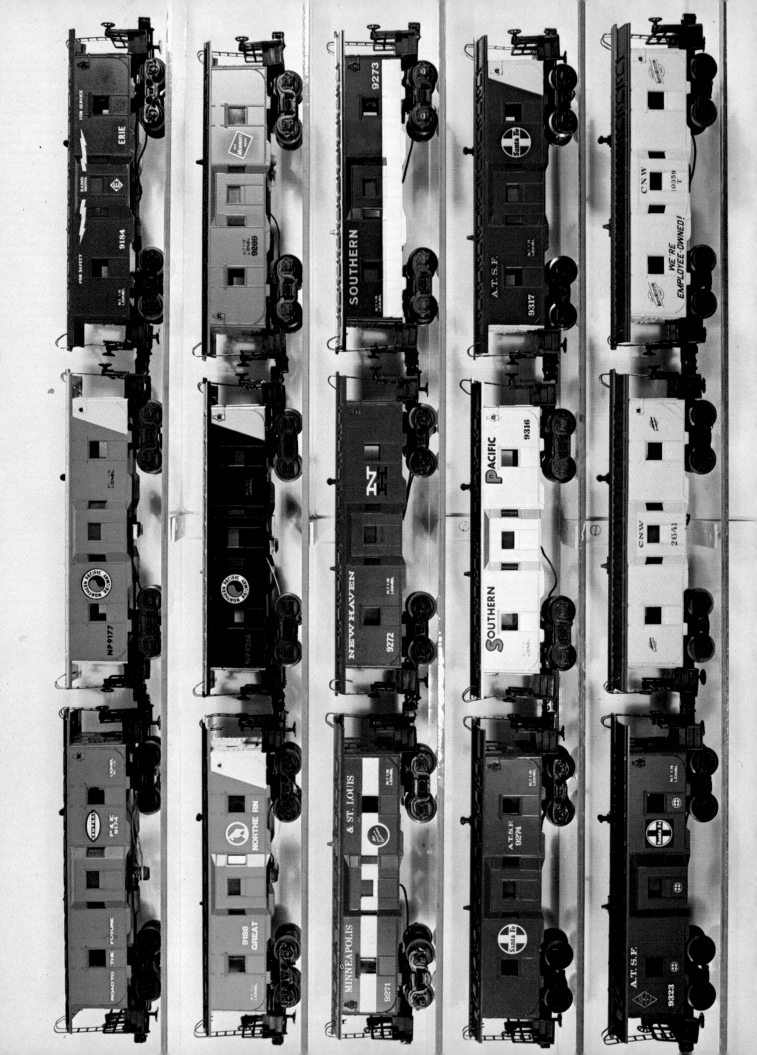

9184 Erie
9269 Milwaukee Road
9273 Southern
9317 Santa Fe
Chicago & North Western (Sherry)

9268 Northern Pacific
9272 New Haven
9316 Southern Pacific
Chicago & North Western (Sherry)

9188 Great Northern
9271 Minneapolis & St. Louis
9274 Santa Fe
9323 Santa Fe

BAY WINDOW

Next to boxcars, the bay window is the most collected of the rolling stock catagories. Why that is is confusing, because they are all readily available and have no major variations. They are all top-of-the-line cabooses and have excellent graphics. Bay window cabooses that came in sets only and were not offered for separate sale command more money than those that were sold separately. Some of the interesting ones:

9174 New York Central, which came in the Empire State Express set. When this caboose came out collectors thought Lionel had made a mistake because it had the letters "P&E" under the window. Collectors thought the letters should be "P & LE", for Pittsburgh and Lake Erie, a railroad that is part of the New York Central System. It turned out, however, that Lionel was correct, that the "P&E" stood for Peoria & Eastern, a rather obscure Midwestern line which was also part of the New York Central system. "We got a letter from a member of the Lionel Collectors Club of America saying the caboose didn't exist," says Bill Diss, who selected the caboose. "Dan Johns of marketing came to me and asked what the story was and I showed him a picture I had of the real caboose. I sent it on to the LCCA."

9177 Northern Pacific, which came in a 1976 Service Station special.

9259 Southern.

9259 Southern, the 1977 LCCA national convention car.

9274 Santa Fe, came as part of a Year-end Special in 1978. Collectors complained that the caboose, which was based on a real Santa Fe, did not match the new Lionel 8872 Santa Fe SD18. Lionel yielded to the clamor and made a matching blue and yellow caboose, which has no prototypical counterpart.

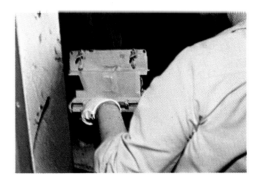

Blue Santa Fe caboose masked while yellow added.

Some readers may wonder about the two Chicago & North Western bay window cabooses shown on page 124. They were not made by Lionel. They were custom-painted by Richard Sherry at the request of Lionel dealer Michael Diedling of Chicago.

Lionel chose to match their Chicago & North Western GP-20 with a round window, NC5-type caboose, which was not correct. The C&NW used bay window cabooses. Diedling, not one to miss an opportunity to sell trains, had Sherry paint over some Lionel Erie cabooses in the green and yellow of the Chicago & North Western so Chicago area customers could buy a matching caboose in the correct style.

Sherry painted 20 cabooses with the "Employee Owned" decal and 41 without the decal.

HO GAUGE

Lionel offered a line of HO gauge for the first time under General Mills management in 1974. The line ran through 1977. It was not a great success, either technically or financially.

"The way we got into HO was based on some real fallacies," says Fundimensions President Jim Boosales. "It was based on the notion that the Lionel name would be magic on any train, that the name on there would allow Lionel to charge more. It was also based on the premise that we would design it from scratch and it would be better than anyone else's.

"It turned out neither of these premises was true. Using an American GE motor that cost twice as much as a Mabuchi motor didn't mean it was better. Our motor was over-engineered. The customer could not appreciate the fact that it could pull 100 cars because that was not what the consumer perceived as quality. The other guy could throw some weight in the engine and it feels the same to the consumer. Why pay more for the Lionel? Our sourcing was weak,

our volumes were low, and our sales force wasn't suited for selling that kind of competitive product."

Lionel will be going back into the HO gauge field, however. Perhaps as soon as 1981. But the product will be cheaper to manufacture and competitive in price with other HO lines.

"Yes, we'll get back into HO," says Boosales. "We have people in the Orient right now finding sources similar to what the competition is using so we can be competitive. What we will do differently this time is really analyze the competition. We have torn their products apart and determined what we can make these same things for.

"I'm not ready to say when the line will be ready because our final marketing proposal hasn't been made to me but it will be soon. We are looking for some promotional vehicle that will allow us to move more trains. What we are looking for is something that says why Lionel should be in this HO business."

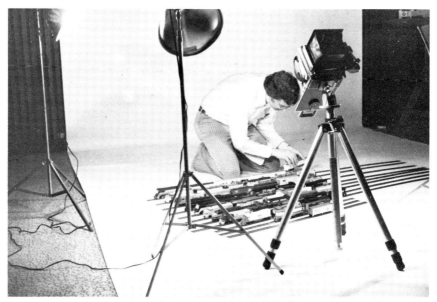

Dave Garrigues setting up HO shot.

2125 Whistling freight shed.

2156 Freight platform (illuminated).

2214 US Steel girder bridge.

2788 Coaling station (kit).

2785 Engine house (kit) with AHM 0-8-0.

2718 Barrel platform, 2720 Lumber shed,
2719 Watchman shanty (all kits).

2797 Rico station.

OTHER THINGS

ACCESSORIES

Accessories were obviously not a priority item of Lionel during the 1970s. The ones that were made were for the most part basic: lamps, crossing gates, block signals, railway stations, etc. The busy, multi-functioned accessories of the '50s and '60s, such as the lumber mill, coal elevator and log loader, were not resurrected.

There are some indications, however, that more complicated accessories may be on the way. A saw mill, which was exactly like the postwar version, was planned for 1980. There was also a hand operated gantry crane, similar to the remote-controled postwar version, scheduled for 1980. Also in the works, probably for 1981, was a barrel loader which was originally made by American Flyer. The increased use of DC power will probably affect accessories, since the DC motor requires much less space and offers the designers some flexibility for placement in the accessories. Jim Boosales appears aware of the value of having accessories.

"The way to sell trains is to make them as fun to play with as possible," he says. "That means kids have to have more to do than watch a train go around a circle of track. We are looking for play value."

The most collectable accessory of the 1970s was the 2125 whistle shed, which came out in 1971. A unit inside the shed produced a train whistle sound. The unit used motors that were left over from the old Lionel. Since there were few of these motors left over, however, there were few of the 2125 whistling sheds made. The old Lionel whistling shed was numbered 125, had a gray base, red roof and was not illuminated. The 1971 version had a brown base, green roof and was illuminated. Both versions had white buildings. The number 2125 was stamped on the base of the new model. In 1976, Lionel came out with a new whistling shed, the 2126, but it was not as good as the old one.

A group of large buildings in kit form was introduced to the line in 1974 and included the Rico Station, which was one of the most popular accessory items to be issued by the new Lionel. These kits were made in Germany and were high quality but they were discontinued in 1977 because they cost too much.

THE BRUTE & SUPER 381

Among the most interesting and valuable of Lionel's prototypes from the old days were a couple of engines that would have been bigger, if they had been produced, than the famous Standard gauge 381, the largest electric Lionel ever made. The story of these prototypes, which have come to be known as "The Brute" and the "Super 381," should have been told in our book on Standard gauge Lionel (Volume III), but it wasn't. The authors have devoted a great deal of thought in search of an explanation why the Brute and Super 381 stories were omitted from the Standard gauge book, an explanation of such basic clarity that the reader would be forced to conclude: "Why, of course! It is perfectly understandable to me how Standard gauge items made in 1928 should be excluded from a book about Standard gauge trains and instead be included in a book about O gauge trains made 50 years later."

We have searched for such an explanation but unfortuantely we have been unable to find one. The truth is we forgot to put it in the Standard gauge book. We have, therefore, decided to put it here. We are, in effect, mopping up. But it is interesting mopping, if we do say so ourselves.

In 1924 Joshua Cowan directed his attention towards the Buddy L company. Buddy L made huge trains and track that was 3¼ inches between the rails. Cowen was turning over in his mind an idea to make an engine that could

The Brute with O gauge Olympian
in the foreground, at John Snyder's home.

run on Buddy L-sized track. He had a prototype model of a Milwaukee Road bi-polar made in Italy. But the thing was a monster. It was about 30 inches long. Cowen scrapped the project as impractical. But he was still concerned about Buddy L and in a mood to experiment with large trains. He had a Standard gauge prototype made up that closely resembled what eventually became the 381, but

The Super 381, photo courtesy of Iron Horse Productions.

it was nine inches longer. Cowen decided that this engine, too, was too big for a child to handle. He then had the prototype 381 made and it was that engine that eventually was put into production in 1928.

The two unmanufactured prototypes eventually found their way into the Lionel Museum, where they remained until the late 1950s when the items there were sold. Don LaSpaluto, a New York City collector, bought them both for $900. LaSpaluto took them to the 1960 TCA convention at Yardley, Pennsylvania and tried to sell them for $1,500, $900 for the Brute and $600 for the Super 381. He did not get his price. As the convention was closing he offered the Super 381 at a reduced price to LaRue Shempp of Williamport, Pennsylvania. Shempp bought it.

"Everybody at the convention thought I was crazy," says Shempp, who now has one of the greatest Lionel collections in existence. "At the time State Sets were selling for $75. In those days collectors were only interested in cataloged items. The hobby was new and nobody knew much about anything. The catalog was their bible. Because the Brute and the Super 381 were not cataloged nobody wanted them."

LaSpaluto eventually sold the Brute to a St. Louis collector who in turn sold it to Bill Vagell, one of the great characters in the collecting hobby. Vagell, who for years ran the Treasure House hobby store in Garfield, New Jersey, and was the top Lionel dealer on the East Coast, is a former professional magician who went by the stage name of The Mystic Craig. Vagell, who is an octogenarian and as sassy as ever ("How do you feel Bill?" we asked him in the fall of 1979, shortly after his 80th birthday. "With my fingers," he replied and did a little soft-shoe shuffle) is one of the leading authorities on Lionel Standard gauge

in the United States. He was the one who gave the name "Brute" to the big Buddy-L-sized monster. He also named the other prototype the "Super 381."

"By the time I purchased the Brute it had been handled a great deal. It had never been painted and I had it electronically cleaned to restore it to its original metal finish.

"You could see the etch marks put on the body by one of the Caruso boys," says Vagell, referring to Mario and Victor Caruso, brothers who came from Italy and started working as solderers for Lionel in 1910 and eventually rose through the organization and were responsible for many inventions along the way. Mario was secretary-treasurer of Lionel when he retired in 1945.

"I had a case made for the Brute and I decided to take it West with me one year when I was going to a magicians convention in Phoenix. On the way I stopped off in Des Moines to see John Synder, another Standard gauge collector. I opened the trunk and showed him the Brute. He flipped. We set it up on his back porch. He just stared at it. 'I've got to have it, Bill,' he kept saying. I didn't want to sell it but he begged me and I did. What the heck."

The Brute now sits in John Snyder's home, where the photograph in this section was taken. The Super 381 is still in the collection of LaRue Schempp. The two prototypes, which nobody wanted at the 1960 TCA national convention, are now among the most prized toy train pieces ever made.

O GAUGE SWITCHES

Lionel planned to bring out O gauge switches in 1980. Early plans called for the switches to sell for between $35 and $50. Realizing that selling switches, a necessary but not flamboyant accessory for operators, is mundane stuff, the marketing department devised a plan to brighten things a bit, and enliven sales. The switches would be sold in boxes that were reproductions of the old boxes of the 1950s.

"It's a nice touch," says Bill Diss. "The graphics and the colors will be the same as on the old box. I have instructed our art department to make them identical except for the number. Even the stock will be that cream color rather than white. Putting them in the old box is kind of a market research deal. I think there will be some additional perceived value with the switches in the old box."

S GAUGE

When General Mills leased the rights to use Lionel's name, the rights to American Flyer were included in the deal, since Lionel had acquired American Flyer when it went out of business in 1967. The question of putting out an S gauge line first arose seriously in 1973.

"I talked with a fellow back then who was chairman of an S gauge collectors club," says Bill Diss. "He wanted us to go into S gauge, naturally. I told him that we had the tooling and we could probably go into production, but that we weren't sure there was a market. I asked him to circulate some petitions, get a bunch of signatures, and I would take them to our management and influence them to go into S gauge. I never heard from the guy again."

Through the years Diss received letters requesting S gauge and finally, for the 1979 line, Lionel decided to put out three cars, a 9100 Gulf tanker, a 9200 Chessie hopper, and a 9700 Santa Fe boxcar. But orders originally were slow.

"After all the letters we had received, we were disillusioned with the response we received orginally, in the spring of 1979," says Diss, "but by summer the response picked up. We then decided to continue the S gauge products for another year, where at first we thought we would not. At this time we do not have plans for an engine or caboose, but if these items continue to go well we will probably add them to the line."

JOHNNY CASH BLUE TRAIN

The Johnny Cash Blue Train was a specially built item presented to singer Johnny Cash in 1973. Cash did the Lionel commercials that year. The background on the train and, incidentally, on how Cash was selected as the voice of Lionel, reads like a Dick Branstner family album.

It was Branstner's wife, Mary, who, when Lionel was looking for a personality to plug its product, suggested Johnny Cash. Mary Branstner knew that Cash had recorded many songs with train themes. She had all of his railroad songs put on one tape and had her husband, who was vice-president of engineering and development, play them for the General Mills executives. According to Branstner, the tape sold the executives on Cash.

"After Cash did all those commericials for us I wanted to do something for him," says Branstner. My father, Bruno, worked for Lionel and was a train designer himself, as well as a scratch builder. When Lionel thought about doing a Mickey Mouse handcar for their 75th anniversary, my father designed the car and made the prototype. Eventually we decided it was too difficult to decorate the figures, too expensive, and the handcar was never made. Anyway, my father built a special loco for Cash. It was a hybrid. It had parts from many different Lionel engines, old and new.

Blue Train, photo courtesy of O Scale Magazine.

"The boiler was the 665 small Hudson. The motor was prewar with prewar wheels. The cab was one of the trial shots we made when we tested the tool for the 665. I picked up all the stuff including the linkage one day when I was in Hillside and asked my dad to assemble it.

"A guy by the name of Bob Olard, who was in the art department at Model Products, painted the engine Blue Comet blue. The trim was all painted gold. I had the nameplate made by a jeweler in Mount Clemens. We called it the Blue Train because there is a passage in one of his songs that goes, 'I want to ride a blue train.'"

The existence of the Blue Train, which now sits in Johnny Cash's trophy room, is not widely known, but what is even less known is the existence of a train made for Johnny Cash's son.

"It had a smaller engine but was painted the same way," says Branstner. "The plaque read 'Johnny Cash Jr.' We gave the kid cars, track, everything. The box we shipped them in must have been five feet-by-five feet-by-five feet. I mean, it was a whole railroad."

1973 TCA CONVENTION CARS

9123 yellow auto-carrier.

Lionel made 68 cars especially for the TCA convention of 1973. There were boxcars, auto carriers, reefers and gondolas which were given away as door prizes. The cars were assigned nine different numbers.

"One day in 1973 Norm Furhm of the TCA came into my office," say Dick Branstner. "I had a bunch of cars on my workbench. I always have a workbench in my office. I was trying out different colors and hot-stamps. Norm asked me what I was going to do with the cars after I finished the tests. I told him they would be scrapped. Norm told me about the up-coming convention and asked if I would make some cars in special colors and markings so they could be given away as door prizes.

"I asked George Toteff and he said. 'Sure, why not?' I made a group of cars with the new line's paint colors and the previous year's hot-stamp colors. Very few were made of each car. A letter came with each saying exactly how many were made."

Ed Barbaret of the TCA went to Mount Clemens and picked up the cars.

"The only way we could get them ready in time for the convention was if I assembled them," Barbaret says. "I picked up the parts from Lionel and spent three nights putting the doors, trucks and bases together."

The winner of the first door prize had a choice between five of the cars or a reproduction of the Ives 1694 loco. The winner chose the 1694 loco.

NO.	CAR	COLOR	MADE
9701	B&O Auto Boxcar	Blue	12
9703	CP Rail Boxcar	Green/blue	5
9705	D&RG Boxcar	Silver/red	11
9705	D&RG Boxcar	Silver/orange	10
9706	C&O Boxcar	Black/yellow	4
9123	C&O Auto Carrier	Yellow/blue	10
9123	C&O Auto Carrier	Blue/white	6
9802	Miller Reefer	Gray/red	5
9820	Wabash Gondola	Gray/white	2
9821	SP Gondola	Black/white	3

O-gauge switch with "new-old" box.

INVENTORY LIST

DIESELS

ALCOS

8020 Santa Fe A 70-76
8020 Santa Fe A D 70, 71
8021 Santa Fe B 71-76
8022 Santa Fe A JCP DSS 71
8025 Canadian National A Canada 71
8025 Canadian National A D Canada 71
8252 Delaware & Hudson A 72
8253 Delaware & Hudson B 72
8351 Santa Fe A 73, 74
8361 Western Pacific A 73-75
8362 Western Pacific B 73-75
8452 Erie A 74, 75
8453 Erie B 74, 75
8552 Southern Pacific A 75, 76
8553 Southern Pacific B 75, 76
8554 Southern Pacific A D 75, 76
8563 Rock Island A Sears DSS 75
8570 Liberty Special A 75
8656 Canadian National A 76
8657 Canadian National B 76
8658 Canadian National A D 76
8664 Amtrak A 76, 77
8667 Amtrak B 76, 77
8861 Santa Fe A 78
8862 Santa Fe B 78

BUDD CARS

8764 B&O Pass 77 SSS
8765 B&O Baggage/Mail 77 SSS
8766 B&O Baggage/Mail 77 SSS
8767 B&O Pass 77 SSS
8768 B&O Pass 77 SSS
8868 Amtrak Baggage/Mail 78
8869 Amtrak Pass 78
8870 Amtrak Pass 78
8871 Amtrak Baggage/Mail 78

F-3 UNITS

8363 B&O A 73-75
8364 B&O A D 73-75
8365 Canadian Pacific A 73 SSS
8366 Canadian Pacific A D 73 SSS
8464 Rio Grande A 74 SSS
8465 Rio Grande A D 74 SSS
8466 Amtrak A 74-76
8467 Amtrak A D 74-76
8468 B&O B SSS
8469 Canadian Pacific B SSS
8474 Rio Grande B SSS
8475 Amtrak B SSS
8555 Milwaukee Road A 75 SSS
8557 Milwaukee Road A D 75 SSS
8566 Southern A 75-77
8567 Southern A D 75-77
8568 Preamble Express A U
8575 Milwaukee Road B SSS
8652 Santa Fe A 76, 77
8653 Santa Fe A D 76, 77
8661 Southern B SSS
8777 Santa Fe B SSS
8851 New Haven A 78,79
8852 New Haven A D 78, 79
8864 New Haven B SSS
8952 Pennsylvania A 79
8953 Pennsylvania A D 79
8970 Pennsylvania A 79
8971 Pennsylvania A D 79

FM UNITS

8950 Virginian 79
8951 Southern Pacific 79
       C&NW 80

GP-7s

8031 Canadian National 71, 72 Canada
8258 Canadian National D U
8353 Grand Trunk 73-75
8356 Grand Trunk D 73-75
8359 Chessie System 73
8454 Rio Grande 74, 75
8455 Rio Grande D 74, 75
8576 Penn Central 76, 77
8750 The Rock 77, 78
8751 The Rock D 77, 78
8758 Southern D 77, 78
8763 Norfolk & Western 77, 78
8774 Southern 77, 78

GP-9s

8030 Illinois Central 71, 72
8250 Santa Fe 72-74
8254 Illinois Central D 72
8255 Santa Fe D 72
8357 Pennsylvania 73, 74
8358 Pennsylvania D 73, 74
8550 Jersey Central
8559 (1776) Norfolk & Western 75
8561 Jersey Central D 75, 76
8654 Boston & Maine 76, 77
8655 Boston & Maine D 76, 77
8665 Bangor & Aroostook U
8666 Northern Pacific SSS
8668 Northern Pacific D SSS
8757 Conrail 77, 78
8759 Erie Lackawanna 77-79
8760 Erie Lackawanna D 77-79
8775 Lehigh Valley 77, 78
8778 Lehigh Valley D 77, 78
8854 C P Rail 78, 79
8866 Minn & St. Louis SSS
8867 Minn & St. Louis D SSS

GP-20s

8352 Santa Fe 73, 74
8355 Santa Fe D 73, 74
8360 Long Island 73, 74
8367 Long Island D 73, 74
8463 Chessie System U
8562 Missouri Pacific 75, 76
8565 Missouri Pacific D 75, 76
8772 G.M.&O. 77
8776 C&NW 77, 78
8779 C&NW D 77, 78
8957 Burlington Northern 79
8958 Burlington Northern D 79

SD-18

8855 Milwaukee 78
8872 Santa Fe 78, 79
8873 Santa Fe D 78, 79

SWITCHERS (NW-2 TYPE)

 634 Santa Fe U 70
1203 B & M TCA U
8010 Santa Fe 70
8111 D.T. & I. 71, 72
8111 D.T. & I. 73, 74
8354 Erie 73
8460 MKT 74, 75
8471 Pennsylvania 74-76
8473 Coca Cola one step 75
8473 Coca Cola two step 74
8473 Coca Cola three step 74
8556 Chessie 75, 76
8569 Soo 75-77
8660 C P Rail 76, 77
8761 Grand Trunk 77
8770 Electromotive Div. 77, 78
8860 Rock 78

SWITCHERS (SMALL)

8350 U S Steel 73-75
8670 Chessie System 76
8769 Republic Steel 77, 78

U36B AND U36C

1776 Spirit Of 76 74-76
1976 Spirit Of 76 TCA
7500 Anniversary 75, 76
8470 Chessie System 74
8560 Chessie System D 75
8564 Union Pacific 75
8571 Frisco 75, 76
8572 Frisco D 75, 76
8573 Union Pacific w/horn D U
8650 Burlington 76, 77
8651 Burlington D 76, 77
8669 Illinois Central 76
8755 Santa Fe 77, 78
8756 Santa Fe D 77, 78
8771 Great Northern 77
8773 Mickey Mouse 77, 78
8857 Northern Pacific 78, 79
8858 Northern Pacific D 78, 79
8955 Southern 79
8956 Southern D 79
8960 Southern Pacific U36C 79
8961 Southern Pacific U36C D 79

ELECTRICS

GG-1s

8753 Pennsylvania 77 U
8850 Penn Central 78, 79

OTHER

8551 Pennsylvania 75, 76
8558 Milwaukee 76, 77
8659 Virginian 76, 77
8754 New Haven 77, 78
8762 Great Northern 77, 78
8859 Conrail 78

STEAMERS

8040 Nickel Plate 2-4-2   70-72
8040 C. N. 2-4-2   U
8041 N. Y. C. 2-4-2   70
8041 Pennsy 2-4-2   U
8042 Grand Trunk 2-4-2   70
8043 Nickel Plate 2-4-2   U
8140 Nickel Plate 0-4-0   U
8140 Southern 2-4-0   U
8141 Pennsy 2-4-2   71, 72
8142 C & O 4-4-2   71
8200 Docksider 0-4-0   72
8203 Pennsy 2-4-2   72, 74, 75
8204 C & O 4-4-2   72
8206 N. Y. C. 4-6-4   72-75
8209 Docksider 0-4-0   72-76
8300 Santa Fe 2-4-0   74
8302 Southern 2-4-0   73-76
8303 Jersey Cent 2-4-2   73-74
8304 Rock Island 4-4-2   73-75
8304 Pennsy 4-4-2   74
8304 C & O 4-4-2   75-77
8304 B & O 4-4-2   75
8305 Milwaukee 4-4-2   73
8308 Jersey Cent 2-4-2   U
8310 Nickel Plate 2-4-0   U
8310 Jersey Cent 2-4-0   U
8311 Southern 2-4-0   U
8500 Pennsy 2-4-0   75, 76
8502 AT&SF 2-4-0   75
8506 Pennsy 0-4-0   75-77
8507 Pennsy 0-4-0 DSS   75
8600 N.Y.C. 4-6-4   76
8601 Rock Island 0-4-0   76, 77
8602 Rio Grande 2-4-0   76
8603 C & O 4-6-4   76, 77
8604 Jersey Cent 2-4-2   U
8701 General   77-79
8702 Southern 4-6-4   77, 78
8703 Wabash 2-4-2   77
8800 Lionel Lines 4-4-2   78, 79
8801 Blue Comet 4-6-4   78, 79
8803 Santa Fe 0-4-0   78
8805 4-4-2 78
8900 Santa Fe 4-6-4   79
8901 UP Not Made
8902 ACL 2-4-0   79
8904 Wabash 2-4-2   79
8905 0-4-0   79

ROLLING STOCK

AUTO CARRIERS
9123 C&O 74
9125 N&W 74
9126 C&O 73-74
9129 N&W 75
9139 PC 77
9145 IC 77
9216 GN 78
9281 AT&SF 78

BOXCARS
6464-500 Timken U
6464-1970 TCA Chicago U 70
6464-1971 TCA Disneyland U 71
7501 Anniv. 75
7505 Anniv. 75
7506 Anniv. 75
7601 Delaware 74-76
7602 Pennsylvania 74-76
7603 New Jersey 74-76
7604 Georgia 75, 76
7605 Connecticut 75, 76
7606 Massachusetts 75, 76
7607 Maryland 75, 76
7608 South Carolina 76
7609 New Hampshire 76
7610 Virginia 76
7611 New York 76
7612 North Carolina 76
7613 Rhode Island 76
7700 Uncle Sam U
7701 Camel 76, 77
7702 Prince Albert 76, 77
7703 Beech Nut 76, 77
7704 Toy Fair 1976 U
7705 Canadian Toy Fair U
7706 Sir Walter 77
7707 White Owl 77
7708 Winston 77
7709 Salem 78
7710 Mailpouch 78
7711 El Producto 78
7712 AT&SF 79
7800 Pepsi 77
7801 A & W 77
7802 Canada Dry 77
7803 Trains n Truckin U
7806 Seasons Greetings 76
7807 Toy Fair 77 U
7809 Vernors 78
7810 Orange Crush 78
7811 Dr. Pepper 78
7813 Seasons Greetings
7814 Seasons Greetings
7815 Toy Fair 78 U
7816 Toy Fair 79 U
9019 P C 78
9019 Toys R Us U
9035 Conrail 78
9037 Conrail U
9040 Wheaties 70-72
9041 Hershey's 70-76 Brown & Maroon
9042 Autolite 72-76
9042 Autolite U
9043 Erie 73-75
9044 Rio Grande 75, 76
9045 Toys R Us U
9046 True Value U
9047 Toys R Us U
9048 Toys R Us U
9052 Toys R Us U
9053 True Value U
9054 J C Penny U
9090 General Mills 71
9200 Illinois Central 70, 71
9201 Penn Central 70
9202 Santa Fe 70

9203 Union Pacific 70
9204 Northern Pacific 70
9205 Norfolk & Western 70
9206 Great Northern 70, 71
9207 Soo Line 71
9208 Canadian Pacific 71
9209 Burlington Northern 71, 72
9210 B&O 71
9211 Penn Central 71
9214 Northern Pacific 71, 72
9215 Norfolk & Western 71
9230 Monon U
9339 GN Box 79
9359 NBA 79
9360 NHL 79
9362 Major League Baseball 79
9365 Toys R Us 79
9400 Conrail 78
9401 Great Northern 78
9402 Susquehanna 78
9403 Seaboard Coast Line 78
9404 Nickel Plate Road 78
9405 Chatahooche Ind 78
9406 D & R G W Cookie 78
9411 Lackawanna 78
9412 R F & P 79
9413 Napierville 79
9414 Cotton Belt 79
9415 Providence & Worchester 79
9416 M D & W
9417 C P Rail 79
9418 GARR Commemorative Car
9600 Chessie 76
9601 IC 76-77
9602 AT&SF 77
9603 Penn Central 76-77
9604 NW 76-77
9605 NH 76-77
9607 SP 76-77
9608 Burlington Northern 77
9610 Frisco 77
9611 TCA 78 Boston U
9660 Mickey Mouse 77-78
9661 Goofy 77-78
9662 Donald Duck 77-78
9663 Dumbo 78
9664 Cinderella 78
9665 Peter Pan 78
9666 Pinocchio 78
9667 Snow White 78
9668 Pluto 78
9669 Bambi 78
9671 Fantasia 78
9678 TTOS Hollywood 78
9700 Southern 72, 73
9701 B&O 72
9701 B&O U Black
9702 Soo Line 72, 73
9703 Canadian Pacific 72
9704 Norfolk & Western 72
9705 Rio Grande 72 Silver
9705 Rio Grande 72 Orange
9706 C&O 72
9708 Post Office 72, 73
9708 Post Office Toy Fair 73, 74
9709 Bangor & Aroostook 71, 72
9710 Rutland 73 ,74
9711 Southern 74, 75
9712 B&O 73, 74
9713 Canadian Pacific 73, 74
9714 Rio Grande 73, 74
9715 C&O 73, 74
9716 Penn Central 73, 74
9717 Union Pacific 73, 74
9718 Canadian National 73, 74
9719 New Haven U
9723 Western Pacific 74
9723 Western Pacific 74 Toy Fair

9724 Missouri Pacific 74
9726 Erie Lackawanna 78
9727 TAG LCCA
9729 Canadian Pacific 78
9730 Canadian Pacific 74, 75
9731 Milwaukee 74, 75
9732 Southern Pacific 79
9733 Airco 79 LCCA
9734 BAR 79
9735 GT 74, 75
9737 Central Vermont 74, 75
9739 Rio Grande 75
9740 Chessie System 74, 75
9742 M & St. L U
9742 M & St. L Season's Greetings
9743 Sprite 75
9744 Tab 75
9745 Fanta 75
9747 Chessie System 75, 76
9748 Canadian Pacific 75, 76
9749 Penn Central 75, 76
9750 D T & I 75, 76
9751 Frisco 75, 76
9752 L & N 75, 76
9753 Maine Central 75, 76
9754 New York Central 76, 77
9755 Union Pacific 75, 76
9757 Central of Georgia U 74
9758 Alaska 76, 77
9759 Liberty Special U
9760 Liberty Special U
9761 Liberty Special U
9762 Toy Fair 1975 U
9764 GT 76, 77
9767 Rail Box 76, 77
9768 Boston & Maine 76, 77
9769 B. & L. E. 76, 77
9770 Northern Pacific 76, 77
9771 Norfolk & Western 76, 77
9772 Great Northern 76
9774 Southern Belle TCA 75
9775 Minneapolis St. Louis SSS 76
9776 Southern Pacific SSS 76
9777 Virginian 76, 77
9778 Seasons Greeting U 75
9779 TCA 1976 U
9780 Johnny Cash U
9781 Delaware & Hudson 77, 78
9782 The Rock 77, 78
9783 B&O 77, 78
9784 Santa Fe 77, 78
9785 Conrail 77, 78
9786 C&NW 77
9787 Jersey Central 77
9788 Lehigh Valley 77
9789 Pickens 77

CABOOSES
BAY WINDOW
9174 New York Central 76
9177 Northern Pacific U
9184 Erie 77
9188 Great Northern 77
9231 Reading 79
9259 Southern U
9268 NP U
9269 Milwaukee Road
9270 NP 78
9271 M & St. L U
9272 New Haven 78
9273 Southern 78
9274 AT&SF 78
9316 Southern Pacific 79
9317 AT&SF 79
9323 AT&SF 79
9326 Burlington Northern 79
    C&NW 80

N5C PORTHOLE
7508 75th Anniversary 75-77
7600 Spirit of 76 74-76
9160 Illinois Central 70
9161 C.N. 72-74
9162 Pennsylvania 73-75
9163 AT&SF 73-75
9165 Canadian Pacific SSS 73
9167 Chessie 74-76
9168 Union Pacific 75-77
9170 N&W 75
9175 Virginian 76, 77
9176 Bangor & Aroostook
9180 The Rock 77
9181 Boston & Maine 77
9182 N&W 77, 78
9183 Mickey Mouse 77, 78
9185 Grand Trunk 77
9186 Conrail 77
9270 NP 78
9287 Southern 78
9288 Lehigh Valley 78
9289 C&NW 78

SP-TYPE
9057 CP Rail 78-79
9058 Lionel Lines 78
9059 Lionel Lines
9060 Nickel Plate 70-72
9061 AT&SF 70-76
9062 Penn Central 70-73
9063 Grand Trunk 70
9064 C&O 71-77
9065 C.N. U
9066 Southern 73-76
9069 Jersey Central 73,74
9070 Rock Island 73, 74
9073 Coke 75, 76
9075 Rock Island (Sears) 75
9076 Liberty Special U 75
9077 Rio Grande 76
9080 Wabash 79
9166 Rio Grande 74, 75
9169 Milwaukee Road SSS 75
9171 Missouri Pacific 76, 77
9172 Penn Central 76, 77
9173 Jersey Central 76, 77
9178 ICG 76
9187 GM&O 77

4-WHEEL BOBBERS
9067 Kickapoo Valley 72
9068 Reading 73-76
9071 AT&SF 77
9078 Rock Island 76, 77
9179 Chessie 76
9357 AT&SF 79

WRECKER CABOOSES
9019 Santa Fe 78
9021 Santa Fe 70-74
9025 D. T. & I. 71-74
9027 Soo Line 75-77
9085 Santa Fe 79

CRANES
9332 Reading 79
9348 Santa Fe 79
9329 Chessie 80

FLAT CARS
9019 Blank 78
9020 Union Pacific 71-78
9022 AT&SF 71-74
9023 MKT 73, 74
9024 C&O 73-76
9026 Republic Steel 75
9120 Northern Pacific 70-72

9121 L&N 71-76
9122 N P 72-75
9124 P & L E 73, 74
9133 Burlington 76, 77
9149 CP 77, 78
9157 C&O 76-78
9158 Penn Central 76, 77, 79
9212 SCL LCCA
9282 Great Northern 78
9285 Illinois Central 77
9333 Southern Pacific 79
9553 W & A 78

GONDOLAS

9017 Wabash 79
9030 Kickapoo Valley 72 Red
9030 Kickapoo Valley 72 Green
9030 Kickapoo Valley 72 Yellow
9031 Nickel Plate 73-75
9032 Southern Pacific 75-78
9033 Penn Central 76
9055 Republic Steel U
9131 Denver Rio Grande 73-77
9136 Republic Steel 72-76
9140 Burlington 70
9141 Burlington Northern 71-72
9142 Republic Steel 71
9142 Republic Steel U
9143 Canadian National U
9144 Rio Grande 75, 76
9283 Union Pacific 77
9284 Santa Fe 77
9315 Southern Pacific 79
9340 ICG 79
9336 CP Rail 79

HOPPERS

6446-25 Norfolk & Western U
7504 Anniv. 75
9010 Great Northern 70, 71
9011 Great Northern 75, 76
9012 T A & G U Royal Blue
9012 T A & G 71, 72
9013 Canadian National 72-76
9015 Reading 73-75
9016 Chessie 75
9018 D T & I 78
9034 Happy Hopper U
9038 Chessie U
9079 Grand Trunk 77
9110 B&O 71, 72
9111 Norfolk & Western 72-74
9112 Rio Grande 73-75
9113 Norfolk & Western SSS
9114 Morton Salt 74-76
9115 Planters Peanuts 74-76
9116 Domino Sugar 74-76
9117 Alaska 75, 76
9118 Corning U LCCA
9119 Detroit & Mackinac U
9130 B&O 70
9134 Virginian 76, 77
9135 Norfolk & Western 71-75
9213 Minn & St. Louis U
9260 Reynolds 75, 76
9261 Sun Maid Raisins 76
9262 Ralston Purina 76
9263 Pennsy 76, 77
9264 Illinois Central 76, 77
9265 Chessie 76, 77
9266 Southern 76
9267 Alcoa U
9276 Peabody Coal 78
9286 B & L E 77
9322 AT&SF 79
9330 Kickapoo Valley 72
9338 Penn. Power & Light

OPERATING CARS

9280 Horse Transport 77
9300 Penn Central 70-73, 77
9301 U S Mail Car 73
9302 L&N Searchlight 73-78
9303 U P Log Car 74-78
9304 C&O Coal Car 74-78
9310 Santa Fe Log Car 79
9311 U P Coal Car
9312 C R Searchlight 79
9305-9303 w/track
9306-9304 w/track

PASSENGER CARS

1973 TCA Obs., Freedom Bell U 76
1974 TCA Pull., Stars & Stripes U 76
1975 TCA Pull., American Eagle U 76
6403 Amtrak Vista Dome 76, 77
6404 Amtrak Pullman 76, 77
6405 Amtrak Pullman 76, 77
6406 Amtrak Observation 76, 77
6410 Amtrak Pullman 77
6411 Amtrak Pullman 77
6412 Amtrak Vista Dome 77
9500 Milwaukee Pull., City of Milwaukee 73
9501 Milwaukee Pull., City of Aberdeen 74-76
9502 Milwaukee Obs., President Washington 73
9503 Milwaukee Pull., City of Chicago 73
9504 Milwaukee Pull., City of Tacoma 74-76
9505 Milwaukee Pull., City of Seattle 74-76
9506 Milwaukee Combo 75, 76
9507 Pennsylvania Pull., City of Manhattan 74
9508 Pennsylvania Pull., City of Philadelphia 74
9509 Pennsylvania Obs., President Adams 74
9510 Pennsylvania Combo 75, 76
9511 Milwaukee Pull., City of Minneapolis 74 Coupon Car
9512 TTOS Pull., Summerdale Junction U 74
9513 Pennsylvania Pull., Penn Square 75, 76
9514 Pennsylvania Pull., Times Square 75, 76
9515 Pennsylvania Pull., Washington Circle 75, 76
9516 B&O Pull., Mountain Top 76
9517 B&O Pull., Capital City 75
9518 B&O Obs., National View 75
9519 B&O Combo 75
9520 TTOS Phoenix Combo U 75
9521 Pennsylvania Baggage 76
9522 Milwaukee Baggage 76
9523 B&O Baggage 76
9524 B&O Pull., Margret Corbin 76
9525 B&O Pull., Emerald Brook 76
9526 TTOS Obs., Salt Lake City U 76
9527 Milwaukee Obs., Roosevelt U 76
9528 Pennsylvania Obs., Truman U 76
9529 B&O Obs., Eisenhower U 76
9530 Southern Baggage 77, 78
9531 Southern Combo 77, 78
9532 Southern Pull., Beauregard 77, 78
9533 Southern Pull., Stonewall Jackson 77, 78
9534 Southern Obs., Robert E. Lee 77, 78
9535 TTOS Columbus Baggage U 77
9536 Blue Comet Baggage, Barnard 78
9537 Blue Comet Combo Halley 78, 79
9538 Blue Comet Pull., Faye 78, 79
9539 Blue Comet Pull., Westphal 78, 79
9540 Blue Comet Obs., Tempel 78, 79
9551 Western & Atlantic Baggage 78, 79
9552 Western & Atlantic Passenger 78, 79
9570 Pennsy Baggage
9571 Pennsy Pullman "William Penn" 79
9572 Pennsy Pullman "Molly Pitcher" 79
9573 Pennsy Vista Dome "Betsy Ross" 79
9574 Pennsy Obs., "Alexander Hamilton" 79
9575 Pennsy Pullman "Thomas A. Edison" 79

REEFERS

7502 Anniv. 75
7503 Anniv. 75
7507 Anniv. 75
9850 Budweiser 73-75
9851 Schlitz 73-75
9852 Miller 73-75
9853 Cracker Jack 73-75
9854 Baby Ruth 73-76
9855 Swift 73-76
9856 Old Milwaukee 75, 76
9858 Butterfinger 74-76
9859 Pabst 74, 75
9860 Gold Medal 74-76
9861 Tropicana 75
9862 Hamm's 75, 76
9863 Railway Express 75, 76
9863 Railway Express 75, 76
9864 TCA 1974 U
9866 Coors 76, 77
9867 Hershey's 76, 77
9869 Santa Fe U
9870 Dutch Cleanser 77, 78
9871 Carlings 77, 78
9872 Pacific Fruit 77, 78
9873 Ralston Purina 78
9874 Miller Lite 78
9875 A & P 78
9876 Central Vermont 78
9877 Gerber 79
9878 Good & Plenty 79
9879 Hills Bros. (Kraft) 79
9880 AT&SF 79
9881 Rath 79
9882 NYC 79
9883 Nabisco 79

STOCK CARS

7808 Northern Pacific 77
7812 TCA 1977 U
9407 Union Pacific 78
9408 Circus Car U
9707 Katy 72, 75
9725 Katy 74, 75
9728 Union Pacific U
9763 Rio Grande 76, 77
9773 N. Y. C. 76

TANK CARS

6315 TCA 1972 U
9036 Mobilgas 78
9039 Mobilgas U
9050 Sunoco 70, 73
9051 Firestone 74, 75
9138 Sunoco 74, 75
9147 Texaco 77, 78
9148 Dupont 77
9150 Gulf 71
9151 Shell 72
9152 Shell 73-75
9153 Chevron 74-76
9154 Borden 75, 76
9155 Monsanto LCCA U
9156 Mobilgas 76, 77
9159 Sunoco 76
9189 Gulf 77
9250 GMCX 71
9277 Cities Service 78
9278 Life Savers 78
9279 Magnolia 78
9313 Gulf 79
9321 AT&SF 79
9331 Union 76, 79
9334 Humble 79
9347 TTOS 79

VAT CARS

9128 Heinz 74-76
9132 Libby's 75-77
9146 Mogen David 77-79

STANDARD "O" CARS

9801 B&O Sentinal Boxcar 73-75
9802 Miller Reefer 73-75
9803 Johnson Wax Boxcar 73-75
9805 Grand Trunk Reefer 73-75
9806 Rock Island Boxcar 74, 75
9807 Strohs Reefer 74-76
9808 Union Pacific Boxcar 75, 76
9809 Clark Reefer 75, 76
9820 Wabash Gondola 73, 74
9821 Southern Pacific Gondola 73-75
9822 Grand Trunk Gondola 74, 75
9823 AT&SF Flat Car 75, 76
9824 N.Y.C. Gondola 75, 76
9825 Schaefer Reefer 76, 77
9826 P. & L. E. 76, 77

"O" SCALE BUILDING KITS

2175 Sandy Andy Gravel Loader 76-79
2717 Short Extension Bridge 77-79
2718 Barrel Platform 77-79
2719 Watchman Shanty 77-79
2720 Lumber Shed 77-79
2785 Engine House 73-77
2786 Freight Platform 73-77
2787 Freight Station 73-77
2788 Coaling Station 76-77
2789 Water Tower 75-77
2791 Cross Country Set 70-71
2792 Whistle Stop Set 70-71
2793 Alamo Junction Set 70-71
2796 Grain Elevator 77
2797 Rico Station 76-77

ACCESSORIES

2110 Graduated Trestle Set 70-79
2111 Elevated Trestle Set 70-79
2122 Extension Bridge 77-79
2125 Whistling Freight Shed 71
2126 Whistling Freight Shed 76-79
2127 Diesel Horn Shed 76-79
2133 Freight Station 72-78
2140 Banjo Signal 71-79
2145 Automatic Gateman 72-79
2151 Operating Semaphore 78-79
2152 Crossing Gate 70-79
2154 Highway Flasher 70-79
2156 Illuminated Station Plat 70-71
2162 Crossing Gate Signal 70-79
2163 Target Signal (2 types) 70-79
2170 Set of 3 Street Lites 70-79
2180 Road Sign Set 76-79
2181 Telephone Poles 76-79
2195 Flood Lite Tower 70-71
2199 Microwave Tower 72-75
2214 Girder Bridge 70-79
2256 Station Platform 73-79
2256 Station Platform TCA 75 U
2260 Illuminated Bumper 71-73
2280 Bumper Spur Set of 3 73-79
2290 Lighted Bumpers Set of 2 76-79
2307 Rotary Beacon 72-74
2310 Mechanical Crossing Gate 73-77
2312 Mechanical Semaphore 73-77
2313 Floodlight Tower 75-79
2314 Searchlight Tower 75-79
2317 Drawbridge 76-79
2319 Watch Tower 75-78
2494 Rotary Beacon 72-74
2710 Billboard Set 70-79
2710 Billboard Set TCA Uncataloged 1976

HO GAUGE

DIESELS

ALCOS

5400 Santa Fe Red & Silver
5401 Great Northern
5504 Freedom Train
5505 Rock Island
5506 Union Pacific w/Nose Decal
5506 Union Pacific w/o Nose Decal
5507 Amtrak
5509 Southern Pacific
5600 Santa Fe Blue & Silver
5613 Canadian National
5614 Great Northern

EMD GP-9

5402 Union Pacific
5403 Gold Chessie
5511 Grand Trunk
5513 American Flyer
5514 Southern
5515 Frisco
5516 Gold Chessie
5610 Chessie Tri-Color
5611 Illinois Central Gulf
5612 Gold Chessie
5700 Penn Central
5710 Norfolk & Western
5711 Southern
5714 Union Pacific

EMD GP-30

5622 Santa Fe
5623 Burlington Northern
5712 Burlington Northern
5715 Conrail

U18B

5520 Soo Line
5521 CP Rail
5522 Rio Grande
5523 Undecorated

STEAM LOCO GS-4 4-8-4

6500 S.P. Daylight
6501 Freedom Train
6502 Western Pacific

ROLLING STOCK

BOXCARS

8400 CP Rail Boxcar
8401 Grand Trunk
8510 Bangor & Aroostook
8511 Spaulding
8512 AMF
8513 Milwaukee Road
8514 Union Pacific
8515 Western Pacific
8516 C&O
8517 Sears
8613 Union Pacific
8614 Grand Trunk
8701 Conrail
8702 Southern
8703 Chessie System
8704 Railbox

CABLE REEL CARS

8620 Bessemer & Lake Erie
8621 Pittsburgh & Lake Erie

CABOOSES

8405 Santa Fe
8406 Union Pacific
8418 Chessie
8419 Great Northern
8503 American Flyer
8600 Chessie
8601 Burlington Northern
8602 Illinois Central Gulf
8603 Santa Fe
8604 Southern Pacific
8720 Norfolk & Western
8721 Southern
8724 Union Pacific

FLATCARS

8413 Union Pacific
8414 Santa Fe
8415 Black — No Lettering
8520 White — No Lettering
      Great Northern 16-Wheel
8760 Union Pacific
8761 Union Pacific 16-Wheel

FREEDOM TRAIN CARS

 41 Showcase Car
101 Display Car
*105 Display Car
110 Display Car
205 Observation
*Came only in Steam set.

GONDOLAS

8407 Rio Grande
8408 Chessie
8409 Norfolk & Western
8410 Southern Pacific
8730 D&RG
8731 Chessie

HI-CUBE BOXCARS

8612 Union Pacific
8710 Rock
8711 Illinois Central Gulf
8712 Burlington Northern

HOPPERS

8417 Burlington Northern
8555 Burlington Northern
8556 D&RGW
8755 CP Rail
8756 Boston & Maine

MECHANICAL REEFERS 50'

8411 Pacific Fruit Express
8412 Railway Express Agency
8540 Gold Medal
8541 Schaefer
8542 Heinz
8543 Frisco
8740 Coors
8741 Budweiser
8742 Tropicana
8743 Schlitz

STOCK CARS

8402 MKT
8570 D&RGW
8571 Rath
8572 Northern Pacific
8573 D&RGW
8574 Southern
8575 New York Central
8770 MKT

TANK CARS

8416 Dow Chemical

WOOD REEFERS

8739 Coors

WORK CARS

3400 Union Pacific Crane
3401 C&O Crane
8404 C&O Work Caboose
8421 Union Pacific Work Caboose
8422 U.P. Crane & Work Caboose set